MORE BEETLES

BOOKS BY J. HENRI FABRE

THE LIFE OF THE SPIDER
THE LIFE OF THE FLY
THE MASON-BEES
BRAMBLE-BEES AND OTHERS
THE HUNTING WASPS
THE LIFE OF THE CATERPILLAR
THE LIFE OF THE GRASSHOPPER
THE SACRED BEETLE AND OTHERS
THE MASON-WASPS
THE GLOW-WORM AND OTHER BEETLES
MORE HUNTING WASPS
THE LIFE OF THE WEEVIL
MORE BEETLES

MORE BEETLES

BY

J. HENRI FABRE

TRANSLATED BY

ALEXANDER TEIXEIRA DE MATTOS
FELLOW OF THE ZOOLOGICAL SOCIETY OF LONDON

NEW YORK
DODD, MEAD AND COMPANY
1922

TRANSLATOR'S NOTE

This, if we count The Life of the Weevil
as the third, is the fourth and last volume on
Beetles in the Collected English Edition of
Fabre's entomological works. The first was
entitled *The Sacred Beetle and Others;* the
second *The Glow-worm and Other Beetles.*

Of the fourteen chapters, part of the four
devoted to the Minotaur appeared, in an
abbreviated form, in *The Life and Love of
the Insect,* prepared by myself for Messrs.
Adam and Charles Black and published in
America by the Macmillan Co. Similarly,
The Pine Cockchafer and the two chapters on
the Gold Beetles occur in Mr. Fisher Unwin's
Social Life in the Insect World (published in
America by the Century Co.), translated by
Mr. Bernard Miall, whom I take this opportunity of thanking for his assistance in the
translation of the present volume. These
seven chapters are included in the Collected
Edition by arrangement with the publishers
named.

ALEXANDER TEIXEIRA DE MATTOS.

CHELSEA, 29 *September,* 1921.

CONTENTS

CONTENTS

MORE BEETLES

CHAPTER I

MY hermitage boasts a long, wide lilac-walk. When May is here and the two rows of bushes, bending beneath their load of clustering blooms, form pointed arches overhead, this walk becomes a chapel, in which the loveliest festival of the year is celebrated beneath the kisses of the morning sun: a peaceful festival, with no flags flapping at the windows, no expenditure of gunpowder, no drunken squabbles; a festival of simple creatures disturbed neither by the harsh brass band of the dance nor by the shouts of the crowd acclaiming the amateur who has just won a silk handkerchief at the hop, skip and jump. Vulgar delights of drinks and crackers, how far removed are you from this solemn celebration!

I am one of the worshippers in the chapel of the lilacs. My orison, which cannot be translated into words, is a tender and intimate emotion. Devoutly I make my stations from one column of verdure to another,

telling step by step my observer's rosary.
My prayer is an "Oh!" of admiration.

To this delicious festival pilgrims have
hastened, to gain the Lenten indulgences and
to slake their thirst. Here, dipping their
tongues by turns into the holy-water stoup of
the same flower, are the Anthophora [1] and
her tyrant the Melecta.[2] Robber and victim sip their nectar like good neighbours.
There is no ill-feeling between them. Both
attend to their own affairs in peace. They
seem not to know each other.

The Osmiæ,[3] clad in black-and-red velvet,
dust their ventral brushes with pollen and
make hoards of meal in the reeds round
about. Here are the Eristales,[4] noisy,
giddy-pated insects, whose wings shimmer in
the sun like scales of mica. Drunk with
syrup, they withdraw from the festival and
sleep off their debauch in the shadow of a
leaf.

[1] One of the wild Bees. Cf. *The Mason-bees,* by J.
Henri Fabre, translated by Alexander Teixeira de Mattos: chap. viii; and *Bramble-bees and Others,* by J.
Henri Fabre, translated by Alexander Teixeira de Mattos: chaps. ii., iv. and vii.—*Translator's Note.*

[2] A parasitic Bee. Cf. *The Mason-bees:* chap. viii.—
Translator's Note.

[3] For these wild bees, cf. *Bramble-bees and others:
passim.—Translator's Note.*

[4] Drone-flies.—*Translator's Note.*

2

The Cetoniæ

These others are Wasps, Polistes,[1] hot-tempered swashbucklers. When these intolerant creatures are abroad, peaceful insects withdraw and establish themselves elsewhere. Even the Hive-Bee, predominating in numbers and ever ready to unsheathe her sting, makes way for them, busy as she is gathering in the harvest.

These thick-set, richly variegated Moths are Sesiæ, with wings not dusted with scales throughout. The bare zones, like so much transparent gauze, contrast with the covered zones and are an added beauty. The sober sets off the magnificent.

Here is a crazy swarm, eddying, receding, returning, rising and falling. It is the ballet of the common Butterfly-folk, the Cabbage Butterflies,[2] all white, with black, eye-shaped dots. They flirt in mid-air, pursuing and pressing their attentions on one another, until, weary of frolic, now one, now another of the dancers alights once more upon the

[1] Cf. *The Hunting Wasps*, by J. Henri Fabre, translated by Alexander Teixeira de Mattos: chap. vii.; and *The Mason-Wasps*, by J. Henri Fabre, translated by Alexander Teixeira de Mattos: chaps. ix and x.—*Translator's Note.*

[2] Cf. *The Life of the Caterpillar*, by J. Henri Fabre, translated by Alexander Teixeira de Mattos: chap. xiv.—*Translator's Note.*

lilacs, quenching her thirst from the amphoræ of the flowers. While the proboscis dives down the narrow throat of the blossom, sucking the nectar at the base, the wings, gently fluttering, are raised above the back, expanding anew and again standing erect.

Almost as numerous but less sudden in flight, because of his wide-spreading wings, is the Machaon, the magnificent Swallowtail Butterfly, with the orange spots and the blue crescents.

The children have come to join me. They are enraptured by this elegant creature, which always escapes their pouncing hands and flies a little farther to taste the nectar of the flowers while moving its wings after the fashion of the Cabbage Butterfly. If the pump is working quietly in the sunlight, if the syrup is rising easily, this gentle fanning of the wings is in all these Butterflies a sign of satisfaction.

A catch! Anna, the youngest of the whole household, gives up all hope of capturing the Swallow-tails, who never wait for her nimble little hand to seize them. She has found something more to her liking. It is the Cetonia. The handsome insect has not yet recovered from the chill of morning; it lies slumbering all golden on the lilac-blossoms, unconscious of danger, incapable of flight. It is plentiful. Five or six are quickly caught. I intervene, so that the rest may be left in peace. The booty is placed in a box, with a bed of blossoms. Presently, during the heat of the day, the Cetonia, with a long thread tied to one leg, will fly in circles round the little girl's head.

Childhood is pitiless because it does not understand, for nothing is more cruel than ignorance. None of my madcaps will heed the sufferings of the insect, a melancholy galley-slave chained to a cannon-ball. These artless minds find amusement in torture. I dare not always call them to order, for I admit that I on my side am also guilty, though I am ripened by experience, to some extent civilized and beginning to know a thing or two. They inflict suffering for the sake of amusement and I for the sake of information: is it not really the same thing? Is there a very definite line of demarcation between the experiments of knowledge and the puerilities of childhood? I cannot see it.

More Beetles

Human barbarity in the past employed the rack to force a prisoner to speak. Am I anything but a torturer when I interrogate my insects and put them to the rack to wrest some secret from them? Let Anna get such pleasure as she can out of her prisoners, for I am meditating something worse. The Cetonia has things to reveal to us, things that will interest us, beyond a doubt. Let us try to obtain these revelations. We cannot, of course, do so without serious inconvenience to the insect. So be it; and now let us proceed: we will silence our kindly scruples for the sake of the story.

Among the guests at the festival of the lilacs the Cetonia deserves to be most honourably mentioned. He is of a good size, which lends itself to observation. Though deficient in elegance with his massive, square-cut build, he has splendour in his favour: the gleam of copper, the flash of gold, or the austere magnificence of bronze as it leaves the brass-founder's burnisher. He is a regular frequenter of my enclosure, a neighbour, and will therefore spare me the trips which are beginning to tell upon me. Lastly—and this is an excellent quality when one wishes to be understood by all one's readers—he is known to everybody, if not by his classic name,[1] at least as an object that often meets the eye.

Who has not seen him, like a great emerald lying at the heart of a rose, whose tender blush he enhances by the richness of his jewellery? In this voluptuous bed of stamens and petals he is encrusted, motionless; he remains there night and day, intoxicated by the heady fragrance, drunk with nectar. It needs the stimulus of fierce sunlight to arouse him from his bliss and set him soaring with a buzzing flight.

To watch the idle Beetle in his sybaritic bed, without further information, one would hardly suspect him of gluttony. What nourishment can he find on a rose or a cluster of hawthorn-blossom? At most a tiny drop of sugary exudation, for he does not browse upon the petals, still less upon the foliage. And can this, a mere nothing, satisfy that big body? I hesitate to believe it.

In the first week of August I placed in a cage fifteen Cetoniæ that had just burst their shells in my rearing-jars. Bronze

---

[1] The Cetonia is also known as the Rose-chafer (*C. aurata*). Cf. *More Hunting Wasps,* by J. Henri Fabre, translated by Alexander Teixeira de Mattos: *Translator's Note.*

above and violet underneath, they belong to the species *C. metallica,* FAB. I provide them, according to the resources of the day, with pears, plums, melon or grapes.

It is a joy to see them feast. Once at table they do not budge. Not a movement, not even a shifting of the feet. With their heads in the fruit-pulp, often with their bodies completely submerged, they sip and swallow night and day, in the darkness, in the sunlight, without a break. Surfeited with sweets, the guzzlers hold on. Collapsing under the table, that is to say, under the deliquescent fruit, they still lick their lips, in the blissful drowsiness of a child that drops asleep with its slice of bread and jam at its lips.

There is no sportiveness in their orgy, even when the sun shines fiercely into the cage. All activity is suspended; the time is wholly devoted to the joys of the stomach. In this torrid heat it is so pleasant to lie under the greengage, oozing with juice! With such good things at hand, why go flying across the fields where everything is parched? None dreams of such a thing. There is no scaling of the walls of the cage, no sudden unfurling of the wings in an attempt to escape.

This life of junketing has already lasted a fortnight without producing satiety. Such a protracted banquet is not frequent; we do not find it even in the Dung-beetles, who are zealous eaters. When the Sacred Beetle, spinning his little unbroken cord of intestinal refuse, has remained a whole day on a tasty morsel, it is the most that the gormandizer can allow himself.[1] But my Cetoniæ have been feasting on the sweets of the plum and pear for a full fortnight; and there is no sign yet that they have had enough. When will the orgy make way for the wedding and the cares of the future?

Well, there will be no wedding and no family-cares this year. These are put off till next year: a singular postponement, quite at variance with the usual custom, which is to be extremely expeditious in these important matters. It is the season of fruits; and the Cetonia, a passionate glutton, means to enjoy these good things without

---

[1] Cf. *The Sacred Beetle and Others*, by J. Henri Fabre, translated by Alexander Teixeira de Mattos: chaps. i to vii. and in particular chap. iv.—*Translator's Note.*

being diverted from them by the worries of egg-laying. The gardens offer the luscious pear and the wrinkled fig, its eye moist with syrup. The greedy creature takes possession of them and becomes oblivious to all else.

However, the dog-days are becoming more and more pitiless. Day after day, another load of brushwood, as our peasants say, is added to the furnace of the sun. Excessive heat, like cold, produces a suspension of life. To kill the time, creatures that are grilled or frozen go to sleep. The Cetoniæ in my breeding-cage bury themselves in the sand, a couple of inches down. The sweetest fruits no longer tempt them: it is too hot.

It takes the moderate temperature of September to wake them from their torpor. At this season they reappear on the surface; they settle down to my bits of melon-rind, or slake their thirst at a small bunch of grapes, but soberly, taking only short draughts. The hunger-fits of early days and the interminable filling of the belly have gone for ever.

Now comes the cold weather. Again my captives disappear underground. Here they pass the winter, protected only by a layer of sand a few inches in depth. Under this slight covering, in their wooden shelter, exposed to all the winds of heaven, they are not endangered by the severe frosts. I thought them susceptible to cold, but I find that they bear the hardships of the winter remarkably well. They have retained the robust constitution of the larvæ, which I used to find, to my astonishment, lying stiff and stark in a block of frozen snow, yet returning to life when carefully thawed.

March is not over before signs of life reappear. My buried Beetles emerge, climb up the wire trellis, wandering about if the sun is kind, going back into the sand if the air grows colder. What am I to give them? There is no fruit. I serve them some honey in a paper dish. They go to it without any marked assiduity. Let us find something more to their taste. I offer them some dates. The exotic fruit, a delicious pulp in a thin skin, suits them very well, despite its novelty: they could set no greater store by pears or figs. The dates bring us to the end of April, the time of the first cherries.

We have now returned to the regulation diet, the fruits of the country. A very moderate consumption takes place: the hour is past for feats of gastric prowess. Very soon my boarders grow indifferent to food. I surprise them in nuptial embraces, a sign that egg-laying is near at hand. In anticipation of events, I have placed in the cage, level with the soil, a pot full of dead, half-rotten leaves. About the summer solstice I see them enter it, one by one, remaining in it for some little time. Then, having finished their business, they return to the surface. For a week or two longer, they wander about, finally hiding themselves in the sand, at no great depth, and dying.

Their successors are in the pot of rotten leaves. Before the end of June I find, in the tepid mass, plenty of recent eggs and very young larvæ. I now have the explanation of a peculiarity which caused me some confusion at the time of my earlier studies. When rummaging through the big heap of leaf-mould which, in a shady corner of the garden, provides me yearly with a rich colony of Cetoniæ, I used to find, under my trowel, in July and August, intact cocoons which would soon split open under the thrust of the insect inside; I also found the adult Cetonia, who had emerged from her strong-box that very day, and quite close to these I would find very young larvæ, which had only just made their appearance. I had before my eyes the crazy paradox of children born before their parents.

The breeding-cage has cleared up these obscure points completely. It has taught me that the Cetonia, in the adult form, lives through a whole year and the summer of the following year. The cocoon is broken during the summer heats of July and August. The regular thing would be, provided the season were propitious, to think at once of the family, after indulging in a few nuptial frolics. This is the general rule among other insects. For them the present form is an efflorescence of brief duration, which the needs of the future employ as quickly as may.

The Cetonia does not display this haste. She was a gross eater in her days of pot-bellied grubhood; she remains a gross eater beneath the splendour of her adult cuirass. She spends her life, so long as the heat is not too overwhelming, in the jam-factory of the orchard: apricots, pears, peaches, figs and plums. Lingering over her meal, she forgets all else and defers her egg-laying to the following year.

After the torpor of hibernation in some place of shelter, she reappears with the first days of spring. But there is no fruit now; and last year's glutton, who, for that matter, has become a frugal eater, whether by necessity or by temperament, has no other resource than the niggardly drinking-bar of the flowers. When June has come, she sows her eggs in a heap of vegetable mould, beside the chrysalids whence the adult insect will emerge a little later. This being so, unless we are in the secret, we behold the mad spectacle of the egg preceding the mother that lays it.

Among the Cetoniæ that make their appearance in the course of the same year we must therefore distinguish two generations. Those of the spring, the inhabitants of the roses, have lived through the winter. They must lay their eggs in June and then die. Those of the autumn, passionate fruit-lovers, have recently left their nymphal dwellings. They will hibernate and will lay their eggs about the middle of the following summer.

We have come to the longest days of the year; this is the moment. In the shadow of the pines, against the wall of the enclosure, stands a heap some cubic yards in volume, formed of all the rubbish of the garden and particularly of dead leaves collected at the time of their fall. This is the compost-factory which supplies the needs of my potted plants. Now this bank of corruption, warmed by the slow decomposition which is working in it, is a paradise for the Cetoniæ in their larval state. The fat grub swarms there, finding abundant provender in the shape of fermented vegetable matter and an agreeable warmth, even in the heart of the winter.

Four species live here, thriving admirably, despite the annoyance which my curiosity causes them. The most numerous is the Metallic Cetonia (*C. metallica,* FAB.). This is the insect that provides me with the greater part of my data. The others are the common Golden Cetonia, or Rose-chafer (*C. aurata,* LINN.), the Dark-brown Cetonia (*C. morio,* FAB.) and lastly the small Funeral-pall Cetonia (*C. stictica,* LINN.).[1]

Let us inspect the heap about nine or ten o'clock in the morning. We must be diligent and patient, for the advent of the laying mothers is subject to capricious delays

[1] This Beetle, also known as *C. Oxythyrea,* MULS., is black and, in the males, covered with white spots, suggesting a pall.—*Translator's Note.*

and often makes us wait in vain. Chance favours us. Here is a Metallic Cetonia dropping in from some neighbouring spot. In wide circles she flies once or twice over the heap; she inspects the lie of the land from above and selects a point easy of access. Whoosh! She pounces upon it, digs with her head and legs and forthwith makes her way in. Which way will she go?

At first the sense of hearing tells us of the direction followed: we hear a rustling of withered leaves as long as the insect is working through the dry outer layer. Then nothing but silence: the Cetonia has reached the moist centre of the heap. Here and here only must the laying take place, so that the grub emerging from the egg may find soft food at hand without seeking for it. Let us leave the mother to her task and return a couple of hours later.

But first let us reflect upon what has just occurred. A magnificent insect, a living gem of goldsmith's work, was slumbering just now at the heart of a rose, on the satin of its petals, in the sweetness of its scent. And now this voluptuary in her golden tunic, this sipper of ambrosia, suddenly leaves her flower and buries herself in corruption; she

16

abandons the sumptuous hammock, fragrant of attar, to burrow in nauseous filth. Whence this sudden depravity?

She knows that her grub will regale itelf on what she herself abhors; and overcoming her repugnance, not even giving it a thought, she takes the plunge. Is she actuated by the memory of her larval days? But what memory of food can she have after a year's interval, above all after an absolute remoulding of her organism? To draw the Cetonia hither, to make her come from the rose to this putrid heap, there is something better than the memory of the belly; there is a blind, irresistible impulse, which acts in the most logical manner under cover of a seeming insanity.

Let us now return to the heap of leaf-mould. The rustle of the withered leaves has informed us approximately: we know in what direction to make our search, a minute and hesitating search, for we have to follow the mother's trail. Nevertheless, guided by the materials thrust aside on the insect's passage, we reach our goal. The eggs are found, scattered without order, always singly, with no preparatory measures. It is enough that there should be close at hand soft vegetable matter, suitably fermented.

The egg is an ivory globule, departing only slightly from the spherical form and measuring nearly three millimetres [1] in diameter. The hatching takes place twelve days later. The grub is white, bristling with short, sparse hairs. When laid bare and removed from its leaf-mould, it crawls upon its back, that is to say, it possesses the curious method of locomotion characteristic of its race. With its earliest wriggles it proclaims the art of walking on its back, with its legs in the air.

Nothing is easier than to rear this grub. A thin box, which hinders evaporation and keeps the provisions fresh, receives the nurseling together with a selection of fermented leaves, gathered from the heap of mould. This is enough: my charge thrives and undergoes its transformation in the following year, provided I take care to renew the victuals from time to time. No entomological rearing gives less trouble than that of the Cetonia-larva, with its robust appetite and its vigorous constitution.

Its growth is rapid. At the beginning of August, four weeks after hatching, the grub

[1] .117 inch.—*Translator's Note.*

has reached half its final size. The idea occurs to me to estimate its consumption of food by means of the stercoral granules which collect in the box from the time of its first mouthful. I find, 11,978 cubic milli-metres;[1] that is to say, in one month the grub has digested a volume of matter equivalent to several thousand times its own initial bulk.

The Cetonia-grub is a mill that is always grinding dead vegetable substances into meal; it is a crushing-machine of great efficiency, which night and day, almost all the year round, shreds and powders the matter which fermentation has already re-duced to tatters. In the rotting heap the fibres and veins of the leaves would remain intact indefinitely. The grub takes posses-sion of these refractory remnants; with its excellent shears it tears and minces them very small; it dissolves them, reducing them to a paste in the intestines, and adds them, henceforth capable of being used, to the riches of the soil.

In the larval stage, the Cetonia is a most active manufacturer of leaf-mould. When the metamorphosis occurs and I review the results of my insect-rearing for the last time,

[1] 732 cubic inches.—*Translator's Note.*

More Beetles

I am shocked by the amount of eating which my gormandizers have done in the course of their lives; it can be measured by the bowlful.

The Cetonia-larva is worth attention from another point of view. It is a corpulent grub, an inch long, with a convex back and a flat belly. The dorsal surface is wrinkled with thick folds, on which the sparse hairs stand erect like the bristles of a brush; the ventral surface is smooth, covered with a fine skin, through which the ample wallet of ordure shows as a brown patch. The legs are very well-shaped, but are small, feeble and out of proportion to the rest of the body.

The creature is given to coiling itself into a closed ring. This is a posture of repose, or rather of anxiety and defence. At such times the living coil contracts so violently that we fear to see it burst open and void its entrails when we seek to unroll it by force. When no longer molested, the grub unrolls itself, straightens out and makes haste to escape.

Then a surprise awaits us. If placed upon the table, the harassed creature travels on its back with its legs in the air, inactive.

The Cetoniæ

This extravagant method, contrary to the accepted usages of locomotion, appears at first sight an accident, a chance manœuvre of the bewildered animal. Not at all: it is a normal manœuvre; and the grub knows no other. You turn it over on its belly, hoping to see it progress in the customary fashion. Your attempts are useless: obstinately it lies down on its back again, obstinately it crawls along in a reversed position. Nothing will persuade it to walk on its legs. Either it will remain motionless, coiled into a circle, or, straightening itself out, it will travel upside down. This is its way of doing things.

Leave it undisturbed on the table. It sets off, longing to bury itself in the soil and escape from its tormentor. Its progress is by no means slow. The dorsal pads, actuated by a powerful layer of muscle, give it a hold even on a smooth surface, thanks to their brush-like tufts of hair. They are ambulacra which, by their multiplicity, exert a vigorous traction.

The moving mechanism is apt to roll from side to side. By reason of the rounded form of the back, the grub sometimes turns turtle. The accident is not serious. With a heave of its loins, the capsized grub at once recovers its balance and resumes its dorsal crawl, accompanied by a gentle swaying to right and left. It also pitches to and fro. The prow of the vessel, the larva's head, rises and falls in measured oscillations. The mandibles open and bite at space, apparently trying to seize some support which is lacking.

Let us give it this support: not in the leaf-mould, whose opacity would hide what I want to see, but in a transparent medium. I happen to have what I need, a glass tube of some length, open at both ends and of a gradually diminishing calibre. At the large end the grub enters comfortably; at the other end it finds a very tight fit.

As long as the tube is more than wide enough, the grub moves along on its back. Then it enters a part of the tube whose calibre is equal to that of its body. From this moment the locomotion loses its abnormal character. No matter what its position, whether the belly is uppermost, undermost or to one side, the grub advances. I see the muscular waves of the dorsal pads moving with a beautiful regularity, like the ripples spreading over a calm sheet of water which has been disturbed by the fall of a pebble.

The Cetoniæ

I see the bristles bowing and standing up again like corn waving in the wind.

The head oscillates evenly. The tips of the mandibles are used as a crutch which measures the paces in advance and gives stability by obtaining a purchase of the walls. In all the positions, which I vary at will by turning the tube between my fingers, the legs remain inactive even when they touch the supporting surface. Their part in locomotion is almost *nil*. What use, then, can they be? We shall see presently.

The transparent channel in which the larva is worming its way tells us what happens in the heart of the heap of garden-mould. Supported on every side at once, close-sheathed in the substance traversed, the grub progresses in the normal position as often as in the reversed position and even oftener. By virtue of its dorsal waves, which come into contact with the surrounding materials in every direction, it moves back or belly uppermost, indifferently. Here are no longer fantastic exceptions; matters return to their habitual order; if we could see the grub ambling through the heap of rotting leaves, we should not regard it as in any way peculiar.

But, when we expose it on the table, we perceive a glaring anomaly, which disappears upon reflection. Support is lacking on every side save from below. The dorsal pads, the principal ambulacra, take contact with this one surface; and the .animal straightway walks upside down. The Cetonia-grub surprises us by the strangeness of its locomotion merely because we are observing it outside its usual environment. It is thus that the other corpulent, short-legged grubs would travel—the grubs of the Cockchafer, the Oryctes [1] or the Anoxia-beetle—were it possible to unroll them entirely and to straighten out the crook of their mighty paunches.

In June, which is laying-season, the old larvæ that have lived through the winter make their preparations for the transformation. The nymphal caskets are contemporary with the ivory globules from which the new generation will emerge. Although rudely made, the Cetonia-cocoons are not without a certain elegance. They are ovoids almost the size of a Pigeon's egg. Those of the Funeral-pall Cetonia, the smallest of the species inhabiting my heap of leaf-

[1] The Rhinoceros-Beetle.—*Translator's Note.*

mould, are very much smaller, hardly larger than a cherry.

All, however, have the same shape and the same appearance, so much so that, with the exception of the small cocoons of the Funeral-pall Cetonia, I cannot distinguish one from the other. Here the work tells me nothing of the worker; I must wait until the adults come out to name my discoveries correctly. However, as a general rule, subject to many exceptions, the cocoons of the Golden Cetonia have an outside facing of the insect's droppings, set close together without any definite arrangement. Those of the Metallic Cetonia and the Dark-brown Cetonia are covered with remnants of decayed leaves.

We must regard these differences as resulting merely from the materials that surround the grub at the moment when it is building its cocoon and not from a special method of construction. It seems to me that the Golden Cetonia likes building in the midst of its old dejecta, now hard granules, while the other two prefer cleaner spots. Hence, no doubt, the diversity of the outer layer.

In the case of the three larger Cetoniæ,

the cocoons are free, that is to say, they do not adhere to a fixed base; they are constructed without a special foundation. The Funeral-pall Cetonia has other methods. If it finds in the leaf-mould a little stone, no larger than a finger-nail, it will by preference build its hut on this; but, if there is no little stone, it can quite well dispense with it and build as the others do, without any firm support.

The inside of the cocoon is smooth as stucco, as is required by the delicate skin first of the grub, then of the nymph. The wall is tough, resisting the pressure of the finger. It consists of a brown, homogeneous material, of a nature which at first is difficult to determine. It must have been a smooth paste which the grub worked in its own fashion, even as the potter works his clay.

Does the ceramic art of the Cetonia likewise employ some sort of fuller's earth? So we should judge from the books, which agree in regarding the cocoons of the Cockchafer, the Oryctes, the Cetonia and other Beetles as earthy structures. The books, which are generally compilations and not collections of facts directly observed, do not inspire me with much confidence. In this instance my doubts are increased, for the Cetonia-larva could not find the necessary clay within a short radius, in the midst of the decayed leaves around it.

I myself, digging this way and that in the heap, should be greatly put to it to collect enough plastic material to fill a thimble. What of the grub, which no longer stirs from its place when the time has come to shut itself up in a cocoon? It can gather only immediately around it. And what does it find? Solely remains of leaves, humus, a bad mortar that does not set. The conclusion is inevitable: the grub must have other resources.

To divulge these resources will perhaps expose me to the foolish accusation of unblushing realism. Certain ideas shock us though they are quite straightforward and consistent with the sacred simplicity of things. Nature has not our scruples: she makes direct for her goal, heedless of our approval and our dislike. Let us silence a delicacy which seems out of place: we must ourselves become animals to a certain small extent, if we wish to understand the beautiful economy of animal industry. Let us gloss over things as best we can, but let us not shrink from the truth.

The Cetonia-larva is about to build itself a strong-box in which the transformation, the most delicate of tasks, will be accomplished; it is about to erect itself an enclosing wall, I might almost say, to spin itself a cocoon. The caterpillar, to weave its cocoon withal, has silk-tubes and a spinneret. The Cetonia-larva, which cannot make use of outside things, has nothing at all, it would seem. But this is a mistake. Its poverty is only apparent. Like the caterpillar, it has secret reserves of building-materials; it has even a spinneret, but at the other end of its body. Its store of cement is its intestine.

The grub was a mighty evacuator in its active period, as is proved by the brown granules which it has scattered in profusion along its road. As the transformation approached, it became more moderate; it began to save up, amassing a hoard of paste of a most fine and binding quality. Observe the tip of its belly as it withdraws from the world. You will see a wide dark patch. This is the bag of cement showing through its skin. This store, so well provided, tells us plainly in what the artisan specializes:

the Cetonia-larva works exclusively in fæcal masonry.

If proofs were needed, here they are. I isolate some larvæ which have attained their full maturity and are ready to build, in small jars, placing one in each. As building needs a support, I provide each jar with some slight contents, which can easily be removed. One receives some cotton-wool, chopped small with the scissors; another some bits of paper, the size of a lentil; a third some pars-ley-seed; a fourth some radish-seed. I use whatever comes to hand, without preference for this or that.

The larvæ do not hesitate to bury them-selves in these surroundings, which their race has never frequented. There is here no earthy matter, such as we should expect to find used in the construction of the co-coons; there is no clay to be collected. Everything is perfectly clean. If the grub builds, it can only do so with mortar from its own factory. But will it build?

To be sure it will and supremely well. In a few days' time I have magnificent co-coons, as strong as those that I extracted from the leaf-mould. They are, moreover, much prettier in appearance. In the flask containing cotton-wool, they are clad in a fluffy fleece; in that containing bits of paper, they are covered with white tiles, as though they had been snowed upon; in those containing radish or parsley-seed they have the look of nutmegs embellished with an accurate milling. This time the work is really beautiful. When human artifice assists the talent of the stercoral artist, the result is a pretty toy.

The outer wrapper of paper scales, seeds or tufts of cotton-wool adheres fairly well. Beneath it is the real wall, consisting entirely of brown cement. The regularity of the shell gives us at first the idea of an intentional arrangement. The same idea occurs to us if we consider the cocoon of the Golden Cetonia, which is often prettily adorned with a rubble of droppings. It looks as though the grub collected from all around such building-stones as suit its purpose and encrusted them piecemeal in the mortar to give greater strength to the work.

But this is not so at all. There is no mosaic-work. With its round rump the larva presses back the shifting material on every side; it adjusts it, levels it by simple pressure and then fixes it, at one point after another, by means of its mortar. Thus it obtains an egg-shaped cavity which it reinforces at leisure with fresh layers of plaster, until its excremental reserves are exhausted. Everything that is reached by the trickling of the cement sets like concrete and henceforth forms part of the wall, without any further intervention by the builder.

To follow the grub through the whole course of its labours is impracticable: it works under a roof, protected from our indiscretion. But we can at least surprise the essential secret of its method. I select a cocoon whose softness indicates that the work is not yet completed. I make a moderate hole in it. If it were too wide, the breach would discourage the occupant and would make it impossible for the grub to repair its shattered roof, not for lack of materials, but for want of support.

Let us make a cautious incision with the point of a penknife and look. The grub is rolled into a hook which is almost closed. Feeling uneasy, it puts its head to the skylight which I have opened and investigates what has happened. The accident is soon perceived. Thereupon the hook closes entirely, the opposite poles of the grub come into mutual contact and then and there the builder is in possession of a pellet of cement which the stercoral factory has that moment furnished. To display such prompt obedience the intestine must certainly be peculiarly obliging. That of the Cetonia-larva is very highly so; directly it is called upon to act, it acts.

Now the true function of the legs is revealed. Of no use for walking, they become precious auxiliaries when the time comes for building. They are tiny hands that seize the piece gathered by the mandibles, turn it over and over, and hold it while the mason subdivides it and applies it economically. The pincers of the mandibles serve as a trowel.

They cut bit after bit from the lump, chewing and kneading the material and then spreading it on the edge of the breach. The forehead presses and smooths it as it is laid. When the supply of the moment is exhausted, the grub, coiling itself again into a closed hook, will obtain a further piece from its warehouse, which remains obedient to its orders.

The little that the breach allows us to see—for it is pretty quickly repaired—tells

us what goes on under ordinary conditions.
Without the aid of sight, we see the grub
evacuating at intervals and renewing its
store of cement ; we can follow it as it gathers the clod with the tips of its mandibles,
squeezing it with its legs, dividing it to its
liking and spreading it with its mouth and
forehead on the weak spots of the wall. A
rolling motion of the rump gives it a polish.
Without borrowing any extraneous materials, the builder finds within itself the building-stones of its edifice.

A similar stercoral talent is the portion
of other big-bellied larvæ, which wear
around their abdomen a wide brown sash,
the insignia of their craft. With the contents of their intestinal wallet they build
the hut in which metamorphosis takes place.
All tells us of the high economy which
knows the secret of turning the abject into
the decent and of producing from a box of
ordure the Golden Cetonia, the guest of the
roses and the glory of the spring.

CHAPTER II

SAPRINI, DERMESTES AND OTHERS

TWENTY thousand, Réaumur [1] tells us, twenty thousand embryos in the body of the Grey Flesh-fly! [2] Twenty thousand! What does she want with this formidable family? With offspring that reproduce themselves several times in a year, does she intend to dominate the world? She would be capable of it. Speaking of the Bluebottle,[3] who is far less prolific, Linnæus [4] already wrote:

"Three Flies consume the carcase of a Horse as quickly as a Lion could do it."

What could not the other accomplish?

[1] René Antoine Ferchault de Réaumur (1683-1757), the French physicist and naturalist, inventor of the Réaumur thermometer and author of *Mémoires pour savoir à l'histoire naturelle des insectes.*—*Translator's Note.*

[2] Cf. *The Life of the Fly*, by J. Henri Fabre, translated by Alexander Teixeira de Mattos: chap. x.—*Translator's Note.*

[3] Cf. *idem:* chaps. xiv. to xvi.—*Translator's Note.*

[4] Carolus Linnæus (Karl von Linné, 1707-1778), the celebrated Swedish botanist and naturalist.—*Translator's Note.*

34

Saprini, Dermestes and Others

Réaumur reassures us:

"Despite such amazing fertility," he says, "these sorts of Flies are not commoner than others which resemble them and in whose ovaries we find only two eggs. The maggots of the former are seemingly destined to feed other insects, which very few of them escape."

Now which are the insects charged with this task of extirpation? The master suspects their existence; he guesses that they are there, without having had the occasion to observe them. My retting-vats provide me with the means of filling up this historical gap; they show me the consumers at their appointed task of thinning out the obtrusive maggot. Let me record this tragic business.

A larger Adder is liquefying, thanks to the solvent dribbled by the teeming vermin. The earthenware dish becomes a porringer full of cadaveric fluid whence the reptile's backbone emerges spiral-wise. The scaly sheath swells up and throbs in gentle undulations, as though an internal tide were lifting the skin with its ebb and flow. Gangs of workers pass to and fro between skin and muscle, seeking a suitable spot for their activities. A few of them show themselves

for a moment between the disjointed scales.
Surprised by the light, they dart forth their
pointed heads and at once pop in again.
Close beside them, in the gaps between the
spiral coils, the highly-flavoured broth lies in
stagnant channels. Here the greater part
are feeding in shoals, motionless, packed together, with their bud-shaped breathing-
holes expanded on the surface of the liquid.
Their numbers are indefinite and immense,
defying computation.

Many strangers take part in the maggots'
banquet. The first to hasten to it are the
Saprini, lovers of corruption, as their name
implies. They arrive at the same time as
the Luciliæ,[1] before the flesh liquefies.
They take up their positions, inspect the
body, tease one another in the sunshine, disappear under the corpse. The time has not
yet come for a good square meal. They
wait.

Despite their habit of dwelling in fetid
surroundings, the Saprini are pretty insects.
Well-armoured, thickset, moving by fits and
starts with short, quick steps, they glisten
like beads of jet. On their shoulders are

[1] Or Greenbottles. Cf. *The Life of the Fly:* chap. ix.—
Translator's Note.

chevron-like stripes which the classifier notes
to mark where he stands in the midst of this
specific variety; they temper the brilliance of
their black wing-cases with stippled spaces
which diffuse the light. Some display pol-
ished, shimmering patches on a dull-bronze
background chased as though with the
graver's tool. Sometimes the sombre ebony
costume is embellished with brightly-col-
oured ornaments. The Spotted Saprinus
decorates each wing-case with a splendid
orange crescent. In short, considered merely
from the æsthetic point of view, these little
undertakers' assistants are by no means devoid of merit. They cut an excellent figure
in the glass cases of our collections.

But one should see them above all at
work. The Snake is submerged in the broth
of its liquefied flesh. The maggots are
legion. With their diadem-like valves
gently opening and closing, they lie, spread
like a field of flowers on the pool of meat-
extract. The hour has come for the Saprini to begin feasting.

Busily bustling to and fro on the parts
that are still uncovered, they scale the reefs
and promontories formed by the reptile's
coils and from these points, protected

against the perilous flood, they fish for their favourite titbit. Here is a grub near the bank, one not too large and for that reason all the more tender. One of the gluttons sees it, cautiously approaches the depths, snaps with his mandibles and pulls, uprooting his prey. The plump little sausage emerges, wriggling. As soon as it is on dry land, the victim is disembowelled and rapturously crunched up. Not a scrap is left. The morsel is often shared, two collaborators tugging in opposite directions, but without a scuffle.

Maggot-fishing is carried on in this way at every point of the shore. The catch is not abundant, for most of the fry are some distance from the mainland, in deep waters where the Saprini do not venture. They never risk wetting their feet. However, the tide withdraws by degrees, absorbed by the sand and evaporated by the sun. The grubs retreat under the corpse; the Saprini follow them. The massacre becomes general. A few days later, we remove the Snake. There are no maggots left. Nor are there any in the sand, making ready for the metamorphosis. The horde has disappeared: it has been eaten.

The extermination is so complete that, to obtain pupæ, I have to resort to rearing them in private, guarding the larvæ against the invasion of the Saprini. The earthenware pans in the open air, though thoroughly searched, never yield me any, however numerous the maggots were at the outset. During my earlier experiments, when as yet I had no suspicion of the massacre, I could not get over my surprise when, after noting an abundance of vermin under this or that piece of carrion a few days before, I no longer found anything, even in the sand. I should have concluded that the occupants had migrated in a body, had it been permissible to imagine a maggot making a long journey through a waterless world.

The Saprini, those lovers of fat sausages are entrusted with the task of thinning out the Grey Fly, of whose twenty thousand offspring only a few will survive, just enough to maintain the race within proper limits. They flock about the dead Mole or Adder; but, kept at a distance by the too liquid sanies and, for that matter, able to live on a few frugal mouthfuls, they wait until the maggots' work is finished. Then, the liquefaction of the corpse completed, they slaughter the liquidators. To purge the soil swiftly of life's offal, the scavenging maggot multiplies its legions; then, having itself become a peril by reason of its numbers, it disappears, exterminated, when its cleansing task is done.

In my district, I obtain nine species of Saprini, some found under carrion, others under dung. I give their names in a footnote.[1] The first four species hasten to my earthenware pans, but the most numerous and most assiduous, those on whom the bulk of the work falls, are *S. subnitidus* and *S. detersus*. They arrive as early as April, at the same time as the Luciliæ, whose offspring they ravage with the same zeal as that of the Grey Fly. Both of them abound in my charnel-pits until the torrid sun of the dog-days puts an end to the invasion of the Flies by drying up the exposed carrion too quickly. They reappear in September, with the first cool breezes of autumn.

Flesh or fish, fur, feather or reptile, everything suits them because it also attracts the

[1] Under carrion: *S. subnitidus,* DE MARS*: S. detersus* ILLIG.: *S. maculatus,* ROS.: *S. æneus,* FAB.—*Author's Note.*
Under dung: *S. speculifer,* LATR.: *S. virescens,* PAYK.: *S. metallescens,* ERICH: *S. furvus,* ERICH: *S. rotundatus,* ILLIG.—*Author's Note.*

maggot, their favourite meat. While waiting for the vermin to grow, they take a few sips of the sanies; but these are scarcely more than an appetizer in preparation for the great feast, when the wriggling grubs are fattened to a turn.

Seeing them so active, one at first pictures them as occupied with family-cares. So I believed; and I was wrong. Under the carrion in my necrotic laboratory, there is never an egg belonging to them, never a larva. The family must be established elsewhere, in the dung-hills and dust-heaps apparently. I have, in fact, found their nymphs, which are easily recognized, in March, on the floor of a poultry-run saturated with the droppings of the fowls. The adults visit my retting-pans to feast upon the maggot. When their mission is accomplished, in the late autumn, they seem to return to the filth under whose shelter the generation is prepared which, as soon as winter is over, hastens to the dead bodies of animals to moderate the excesses of the Sarcophagæ [1] and the Luciliæ.

The labours of the Fly do not satisfy the requirements of hygiene. When the soil

------

[1] *S. carnaria* is the Grey Flesh-fly.—*Translator's Note.*

has drunk the cadaveric extract elaborated by the grubs, a great deal remains that cannot be liquefied or dried up by the heat. Other workers are needed, who treat the mummified carcase anew, nibbling at the shrivelled muscles and tendons until the relics are reduced to a heap of bones as clean as ivory.

The Dermestes are charged with this long labour of gnawing. Two species come to my earthenware pans at the same time as the Saprini: *D. undulatus,* BRAHM., and *D. Frischii,* KUGEL. The first, striped with fine, snow-white, wavy lines on a black ground, has a red corselet speckled with brown spots; the second, the larger of the two, is dull black all over, with the sides of the corselet powdered ashen grey. Both wear white flannel underneath, which forms a violent contrast with the rest of the costume and seems inconsistent with the insect's calling.

The Necrophorus,[1] the burier of the dead, has already shown us this propensity for soft stuffs and the clash of discordant colours. He covers his breast with a waistcoat of nan-

---

[1] Or Burying-beetle. Cf. *The Glow-worm and Other Beetles,* by J. Henri Fabre, translated by Alexander Teixeira de Mattos: chaps. xi and xii.—*Translator's Note.*

keen flannel, decorates his wing-cases with red stripes and sports an orange club at the tip of his antennæ. The Wavy Dermestes, wearing a leopard-skin cape and a jerkin striped with ermine, could almost, humble though he be, rival the elegance of this mighty undertaker.

Both of them numerous, the two Dermestes come to my earthenware receptacles with a common aim; to dissect the dead body to the bone and to feed on what the maggots have left. If the work of these is not completed, if the lower surface of the corpse is still oozing, they wait, gathered on the edges of the pan or clinging in long rows to the cords by which it is slung. In their tumultuous impatience, falls are frequent, which throw the clumsy insect on its back and for a moment reveal the white flannel of the belly. The thoughtless Beetle soon recovers his feet, runs away and once more climbs the strings. In the kindly sunshine, frequent pairings occur, which is another way of killing time. There are no fights for the best places and the best morsels. The banquet is plentiful; there is room for all.

At last the victuals are in the requisite

43

condition; the maggots have disappeared, carried off by the Saprini; these last are themselves becoming scarce and are repairing elsewhither in search of another hoard of vermin. The Dermestes take possession of the corpse and remain indefinitely, even during the cruel dog-days, when the excessive heat and drought have put all else to flight. Under cover of the dried-up carcase, in the shadow of the Mole's fur, which makes an impenetrable screen, they nibble and gnaw and clip as long as a scrap of edible matter remains on the bones.

And the work of consuming goes fast, for one of the Beetles, Frisch's Dermestes, is surrounded by her family, who are endowed with the same appetites. Parents and larval offspring of all ages feast higgledy-piggledy, insatiably. As for the Wavy Dermestes, the other's collaborator in the dissection of corpses, I do not know where she lays her eggs. My pans have taught me nothing in this respect. As against that, they tell me a great deal about the larva of the other Dermestes.

All through the spring and the greater part of the summer the adult abounds beneath my carcases, accompanied by the youngsters, ugly creatures covered with wild bristle of dark hairs. The pitch-black back has a red stripe running down the middle from end to end. The white-leaded lower surface already promises the white flannel of maturity. The penultimate segment is armed, above, with two curved points. These are grapnels, which enable the grub to slip swiftly through the interstices of the bones.

The exploited carcase seems deserted, so quiet is everything outside. Lift it up. Instantly what liveliness, what confusion! Surprised by the sudden rush of light, the hairy-backed larvæ dive under the remains, wriggling their way into the crevices of the skeleton ; the adults, whose movements are less supple, run to and fro in their distress, burying themselves as best they can, or flying off. Leave them to their darkness: they will resume the interrupted work and, some time in July, we shall find their nymphs with no other shelter than the remnants of the corpse.

Although the Dermestes disdains to burrow underground in order to undergo their transformation, finding sufficient protection beneath the remains of the wasted corpse, this is by no means the case with the Silpha, another exploiter of the dead. Two species visit my pans: *S. rugosa,* LINN, and *S. sinuata,* FAB. Although assiduously frequented by both species, my appliances tell me nothing definite about the history of these two habitual associates of the Dermestes and the Saprinus. Perhaps I took up the matter too late.

At the end of the winter, indeed, I find beneath a toad the family of the Wrinkled Silpha. It consists of some thirty naked larvæ, glossy, black, flat and tapering to a point. The abdominal segments end on either side in a spike aimed backwards. The penultimate segment has short, bristling filaments. Hidden in the shadow of the disembowelled toad, these larvæ are nibbling the dry meat, long toasted in the sun.

About the first week in May, they repair underground, where each of them digs itself a spherical recess. The nymphs are continually on the alert. At the slightest disturbance, they twirl their pointed abdomen, brandishing it to and fro with a rapid whirling motion. At the end of the same month, the adults leave the soil. Equally precocious, it would seem, are the insects that come to my pans, to eat their fill but not to reproduce their species. Family cares are postponed to a later season, to the end of autumn.

I shall mention but briefly the Necrophorus (*N. vestigator,* HERCH.), whose feats I have described elsewhere.[1] He comes to my apparatus, of course, but without making a long stay, the carcases being as a rule too large for his burying-methods. For that matter, I myself would thwart his enterprises if it did suit him. I want to see not burials but operations in the open air. If the sexton is persistent, I dissuade him by pestering him.

Let us pass on to others. Who is this, assiduous visitor, but appearing only in small parties, hardly more than four or five at a time? It is an Hemipteron,[2] a slender Bug, with red wings and with stout, toothed thighs to its hind-legs; it is the Spurred Alydus (*A. calcaratus,* LINN.), a near kinswoman of the Reduvius, so interesting because of her explosive egg.[3] She too has

---

[1] Cf. *The Glow-worm and Other Beetles:* chaps. xi. and xii.—*Translator's Note.*

[2] An order of insects consisting mainly of Bugs.—*Translator's Note.*

[3] The essay on the Masked Reduvius will appear in the following volume, the last volume of the series.—*Translator's Note.*

an appetite for game, but how moderate compared with the other's! I see her wandering over my specimens in search of a denuded bone bleached by the sun. After finding a suitable point she applies the tip of her rostrum to it and for some time remains motionless.

With her rigid implement, fine as a horsehair, what can she extract from that bone? I ask myself in vain, so dry does the surface exploited appear to be. Perhaps she collects the vestiges of grease left by the Dermestes' conscientious tooth. Quite a secondary worker, she gleans where others have reaped. I should have liked to follow this bone-sucker's habits more closely and above all to obtain her eggs, in the hope of discovering some little mechanical secret at the moment of hatching. My attempts failed. When imprisoned in a glass jar with the victuals which she requires, the Alydus allows herself to pine away from one day to the next. She needs to fly in freedom over the neighbouring rosemary-bushes, after her sojourn in the retting-vats.

We will close this list of undertakers' assistants with the Staphylini,[1] the tribe with

[1] Or Rove-beetles.—*Translator's Note.*

the short wing-cases. Two species, both inmates of dung-hills, haunt my earthen-ware pans: *Aleochara fuscipes*, FAB., and *Staphylinus maxillosus*, LINN. My attention is drawn rather to the latter, the family giantess.

Barred with ash-grey velvet on a black ground, the Big-jawed Staphylinus reaches me only in small numbers, always one by one. She flies up hastily, perhaps from the stables hard by. She alights, coils her belly, opens her pincers and dives impetuously into the Mole's fur. Then, with her powerful nippers, she punctures the skin, now blue and distended by gases. The sanies oozes out. The glutton greedily eats her fill; and that is all. Soon she departs, as suddenly as she came.

I have not had the good fortune to see anything further. The big Staphylinus hastens to my pans only to feast upon a highly seasoned dish. Her family dwelling must be in the dung-hills about the stables of the neighbourhood. I should have much liked to see her make her home in my charnel-pits.

The Staphylinus is a curious creature indeed. Her short wing-cases, covering just the top of her shoulders, her fierce mandibles, overlapping like a meat-hook, and her long, naked abdomen, which she lifts and brandishes in the air, make her a being apart, of alarming aspect. I should like to learn something of her larva. As I cannot do this with the Beetle that visits my Moles, I apply myself to a kindred species, as nearly as possible her equivalent in respect of size.

In winter, when I raise the stones beside the foot-paths, I often come across the larva of the Stinking Staphylinus (*S. olens,* MÜLL.), or Devil's Coach-horse. The ugly animal, which is not very different in shape from the adult, measures about an inch in length. The head and thorax are a fine, glossy black; the abdomen is brown and bristles with sparse hairs. The cranium is flat; the mandibles are black and very sharp, opening in a ferocious crescent whose width is more than twice the diameter of the head. The mere sight of these curved daggers enables us to guess the highwayman's habits.

The creature's most singular implement is the end of the intestine, which is covered with a horny substance prolonged into a stiff tube standing at right angles to the axis of the body. This member is an instrument of locomotion, an anal crutch. In walking, the animal presses the tip of this crutch to the ground and thrusts backwards as with a lever, while the legs struggle forward. Doré,[1] the famous illustrator of extravagant notions, conceived a similar system. He shows us somewhere a legless cripple seated in a bowl supported by a pivot and working himself along on his hands. The artist's grotesque imagination might well have been inspired by the grotesque appearance of the insect.

Even among its own kind, the crutched insect is a bad neighbour. Very rarely do I find two larvæ under the same stone; and, when this happens, one of the two is always in a pitiful state: the other is devouring it as if it were its ordinary game. Let us watch this conflict of two cannibals, each thirsting for the other's blood.

In the arena furnished by a tumbler containing some moist sand, I place two larvæ of equal strength. The moment they face each other, they suddenly rear up, bending their bodies backwards, with the six legs in the air, hooks of the mandibles wide open and the anal crutch firmly fixed. They look

[1] Gustave Doré (1833–1883), the French illustrator of Dante, Rabelais, La Fontaine and many others.—*Translator's Note.*

51

magnificently audacious in this posture of attack and defence. This above all is the best moment for recognizing the great advantage of the pivot at the tail. Though in danger of being disembowelled by its adversary, the larva has no other support than the tip of the abdomen and the terminal tube. The six legs play no part in sustaining it; they wave in the air, all six free and ready to clasp the enemy.

The two adversaries are standing face to face. Which of the two will eat the other? Chance decides. Mutual threats are followed by a hand-to-hand struggle. The fight does not last long. Favoured by the hazards of the fray, or perhaps timing its blows more accurately, one seizes the other by the scruff of the neck. It is done: any resistance on the part of the vanquished is impossible; blood flows and murder has been committed. When all movement has ceased, the victor devours the slain, leaving only the unpleasantly hard skin.

Is this frenzy for killing among creatures of the same species due to cannibalism enforced by starvation? I really do not think so. When well-fed to begin with, rich, moreover, in the victuals which I lavish upon them, these miscreants are as prone as ever to butcher their kith and kin. In vain I overwhelm them with choice morsels: succulent sausages in the shape of young Anoxia-larvæ;[1] Vitrinæ,[2] tiny molluscs which I give them half-crushed, to spare the banqueters the trouble of extracting them from the shell. As soon as they are confronted, the two bandits, which have just been feasting on a prey as bulky as themselves, stand up, challenging each other and snapping at each other until one of the two is dead. Then follows the odious meal. To eat the murdered kinsman is, it seems, the usual thing.

The Mantis[3] who, in captivity, preys upon her mates has the madness of the rutting beast as her excuse. The fierce, jealous creature can find no better way of getting rid of her rivals than to eat them, provided she be the stronger. This procreative depravity is found much higher in the scale. The Cat and the Rabbit notably are prone to devour the young family which might stand in the way of their unslaked passions.

[1] The Anoxia is a Beetle akin to the Cockchafer.— *Translator's Note.*

[2] A genus of Land-Snails.—*Translator's Note.*

[3] Cf. *The Life of the Grasshopper,* by J. Henri Fabre, translated by Alexander Teixeira de Mattos: chaps. vi. to ix.—*Translator's Note.*

More Beetles

In my glass jars and under the flat stones in the fields the Devil's Coach-horse has no such excuse. Thanks to its larval state, it is utterly indifferent to the disorders attendant on the pairing. Those of its fellows which it encounters are not its amorous rivals. And yet without more ado they seize and slay one another. A fight to the death decides which is to be the consumed and which the consumer.

In our language we have the word anthropophagi to denote the horrible eating of man by man; we have nothing to express a similar act in animals of the same species. A proverbial phrase would even seem to say that such a term is uncalled for, except where man is concerned, that baffling admixture of nobility and baseness. Wolf does not eat Wolf, says the wisdom of the nations. Well, here we have the larva of the Stinking Staphylinus giving the lie to the proverb.

What a morality. In this connection, I should have wished to consult the Big-jawed Staphylinus when she came to visit my highly-seasoned Moles, my putrefying Snakes. But she always refused to divulge her secrets, withdrawing from the charnel-pit once she had filled her maw.

CHAPTER III

THE BEADED TROX

THE Fly has deserved well of hygiene. The first to come to the dead Mole, she left behind her a garrison of scavengers which, without dissecting-instruments, whether lancets or scalpels, set to work upon the corpse. The most urgent matter was to sterilize the carcase, to extract from it such substances as are readily corrupted, the source of rapid and dangerous putrescence. And this is what the maggot has been doing. From its pointed mouth, for ever poking and rummaging, it dribbled forth a solvent as effective as any in my laboratory; with this reagent it dissolved the flesh and viscera, or at least reduced them to a thick liquid broth. Gradually the soil is saturated with the fertilizing moisture, which the plant will soon restore to the laboratory of living chemistry.

When her mission is completed, the Fly herself becomes a danger, because of her excessive numbers. In order to perform their pressing task more quickly, the maggots operate in legions. If not checked, they would encumber the world. The balance of things in general demands their disappearance. Then, in due season, the exterminator arrives, the Saprinus doting on fat sausages, the slow-trotting Beetle in black armour who massacres the vermin and leaves only enough survivors to maintain the race.

The Mole is now a dried-up mummy, but is harmful if affected by moisture. This remnant also has to disappear. The Dermestes is entrusted with the task. She establishes herself beneath the remains in company with the Silpha, her collaborator. With her patient tooth she files, rasps and disarticulates as long as a scrap of cartilage is left to gnaw. She is greatly assisted by her starveling larvæ, who are lither in the back and therefore able to slip into narrow crevices.

By the time the Dermestes has finished, my pans contain so many heaps of bones, a conglomeration of Snakes' vertebræ arranged in a row, Moles' jaws, with their fine, insectivorous teeth, Frogs' toe-and-finger-joints, radiating like knotty sticks, Rabbits' skulls overlapping their powerful incisors, all white and clean enough to arouse the envy of the people who prepare our anatomical specimens.

Yes, working one on the soft parts and then the other on the hard, the maggot and the Dermestes have performed a meritorious task. There is no longer any pestilential filth, any dangerous effluvia. The residue, mostly of a chalky nature, if it still offends the eye, is at least capable of vitiating the air, the first aliment of life. General hygiene is satisfied.

Besides his bones, the Mole has left the tatters of his fur; the Snake has been flayed in tatters like the skin which boiling water strips from a fleshy root. The Fly's solvent was powerless to affect these refractory substances; the Dermestes refused them. Will these epidermic shreds remain unutilized? Certainly not. Nature, the sublime economist, takes good care that all things return to the treasury of her works. Not an atom must be allowed to go astray.

Others will come, frugal and patient pickers-up of unconsidered trifles, and will garner the Mole's fur, hair by hair, to cover themselves, to clothe themselves with it; there will be some, we may be sure, that will feast upon the Snake's cast scales. These are the Tineæ, the humble caterpillars of no less humble Moths.

Everything suits them in the way of animal clothing: bristles, hair, scales, horn, fur, feather; but for their labours they need darkness and repose. In the sunshine and bustle of the open air they refuse the relics in my pans; they wait until a gust of wind sweeps the charnel-pits and carries the Mole's velvety down or the reptile's parchment into a shady corner. Then, infallibly, the cast-off garments of the dead will disappear. As for the bones, the atmospheric agencies, having plenty of time, will crumble and disintegrate them in good time.

If I wish to hasten the end of the epidermic remains disdained by the Dermestes, I have only to keep them in a dry place, in the dark. Before long the Moth will come to exploit them. They infest my house. I had received the skin of a Rattlesnake from Guiana. The horrible specimen, rolled into a bundle, reached me intact, with its poison-fangs, the mere sight of which makes one shudder, and its alarm of rattling rings. In the Carib country it had been steeped in a poison which should have ensured its preservation for an indefinite length of time. A useless precaution: the Moths have invaded the thing; they are gnawing at the Rattlesnake's skin and find the unusual dish, here eaten for the first time, excellent. More familiar victuals, such as the skin of our native Snake, tanned by the maggots and the sun, would be exploited with even greater enthusiasm.

And any relics of what has once lived are visited by specialists who come hurrying up to work upon dead matter and restore it to circulation under new forms. Among them are some whose peculiar specialty shows us with what scrupulous economy the waste material of life is utilized. Such is the Beaded Trox (*T. perlatus*, SCRIBA), a humble Beetle, no larger than a cherry-stone at most, black all over and decorated on the wing-cases with rows of protuberances which have earned it the epithet of beaded.

Not to know the Trox is quite excusable, for the insect has never been much talked about. It is an obscure creature, overlooked by the historian. When impaled in a collector's box, it ranks close to the Dung-

More Beetles

Beetles, just after the Geotrupes.[1] Its mean and earthy attire denotes a digger. But what precisely is its calling? Like many others, I did not know, when an accidental discovery enlightened me and taught me that the beaded insect deserves something better than a mere compartment in the collector's necropolis.

February was drawing to a close. The weather was mild and the sun warm. We had gone off in a family party, with the children's lunch, an apple and a chunk of bread, in the basket, to see the almond trees in bloom. When lunch-time came, we were resting under some great oaks, when Anna, the youngest of the household, always on the watch for "beasties" with her six-year-old eyes, called to me from a distance of a few yards:

"A beastie!" she cried. "Two, three, four of them! And such pretty ones! Come and look, papa, come and look!"

I ran up to her. The child had dug into the sand, to no great depth, with a bit of stick, and was breaking up a sort of rag of

[1] Cf. *The Sacred Beetle and Others,* by J. Henri Fabre, translated by Alexander Teixeira de Mattos: chaps. xii. to xiv.—*Translator's Note.*

fur. I produced my pocket trowel and joined her in the task; and in a moment I possessed a dozen Trox-beetles, most of whom I found in a filthy tangle of fur and broken bones. They were working away at it and apparently feeding on it. I had disturbed them at their banquet.

What could this mess be? That was the fundamental question to be solved. Brillat-Savarin [1] declared as an axiom:

"Tell me what you eat and I will tell you what you are."

If I wish to know the Trox, I must first enquire what she eats. Reader, pity the sorrows of the naturalist! Behold me scrutinizing, meditating, conjecturing, my mind set in a whirl by an unspeakable problem, a stercoral problem.

Whom am I to hold responsible for this fibrous lump, in which I seem to distinguish Rabbit's fur as the chief ingredient? The probabilities point to the dog. Rabbits abound on the Sérignan hills; they even enjoy a certain reputation among our epicures. The village sportsmen hunt them assiduously; and their Dogs, those poachers heedless of

[1] Anthelme Brillat-Savarin (1755-1826), the author of *La Physiologie du Goût.—Translator's Note.*

licences and of the police, do not fail to harry them on their own account, at all seasons, close or open.

Two of them are known to me by report: Mirate and Flambard. They meet by appointment of a morning in the market-place, exchange an inquisitive glance, inspect each other with the three regulation turns, lift a leg against the wall . . . and off they go! For the best part of the morning you can hear them on the neighbouring hill-sides, giving vent to short, sharp yelps, close on the heels of a Rabbit who scampers from thicket to thicket, with his little white scut in the air. At last they return home: the result of the expedition may be read on their bloody chaps: the Rabbit was eaten on the spot, just as it was, skin and all.

Does this really explain the substance on which my Trox-beetles were living? It seems to me that it does. Henceforth it would appear an easy matter to rear them. I install the insects in a large earthenware pan with a bed of sand and a wire-gauze cover. The provisions consist of Dog-droppings, dried on the road-mender's stone-heaps beside the highway. My menagerie absolutely refuse to look at them. I have made a mistake. Then what does it want?

It is under hairy ordure that I find the insect, always there and never any elsewhere. Rarely does a lump of this rough felt fail to conceal a few of them. Under their tight-fitting wing-cases, they have only quite rudimentary wings, unsuited to flight. These short-legged creatures hasten to the titbit and gather about it on foot. They come from afar, from all points of the compass, guided by the scent. Once more, what is the origin of this felt, which has a strong enough stench in the fresh state to attract its consumers from such a distance?

At last I have my answer. Investigations patiently pursued on the slopes of the hills, above all near the farms, furnish me with a decisive piece of evidence. This is a mass of filth, full of fur and Trox-beetles, like the others, but this time a regular nugget, all glittering with wing-cases of the Golden Carabus.[1] Eureka! Never did Dog, even though starving, feed on Beetles, least of all on acrid Carabi. Only the Fox, in time of dearth, accepts such food, in the absence of anything better. Later on he makes up for

[1] Or True Ground-beetles. Cf. Chapters XIV and XV of the present volume.—*Translator's Note*.

it with Rabbits, slaughtering them by night, when his rivals, Mirate and Flambard, are resting from their labours.

The fur from which the Fox's stomach can derive no benefit has its votaries. In the natural state, as it grows on the skins which provide the hat-maker with felt, it suits the Moth; unsuccessfully worked by the carnivore's intestine and seasoned with fæcal matter, it delights the Beaded Trox. There are all sorts of tastes in this world, so that nothing may be lost. The menagerie under the wire-gauze dome, when supplied with the requisite diet of Rabbit's fur pickled by an attempt at digestion, fares very well.

Moreover, the food is collected without difficulty. The Fox is only too common in my neighbourhood. I can easily find his furry excreta on the tangled paths which he frequents at night when going his round of the farms. My Trox-beetles have plenty to eat.

Not endowed with a nomadic temperament and abundantly provided for, they seem very well satisfied with the arrangements made on their behalf. By day, they remain on the heap of victuals; feeding at leisure, without moving. If I approach the wire-gauze cover, they instantly drop down; then, recovering from their excitement, they hide under the heap. There is nothing striking in the habits of these pacific creatures, unless it be the pairing, which drags on for two months, frequently broken off, frequently resumed, often a passing fancy. It is never finished.

At the end of April I proceed to search under the heap of provisions. The eggs are distributed very near the surface in the moist sand, singly, without cells or any preparation by the mother. They are white and globular, about the size of small birdshot. I find that they are very bulky in comparison with the size of the insect. Their number is not great. Ten at most is the allowance for one mother, as far as I can judge.

The larvæ soon appear and develop rather quickly. They are naked, cylindrical grubs, dull white, curved into a hook like the Dung-beetles', but without the knapsack in which the latter reserve the cement for plastering the interior of the emptied loaf and preserving the victuals from desiccation. The head is powerful and glossy black; there is a brown streak on either side of the first thoracic segment; the legs and mandibles are strongly made.

Classed close beside the Dung-eaters, the Trox-beetles form a genus of boorish habits, far removed from the domestic fondness of the Scarabæus, the Copris [1] and the others. With them there are no longer provisions stored away beforehand, no rations kneaded for the larva's benefit. The least industrious of the Dung-beetles, the Onthophagi,[2] for example, pack into the bottom of a pit a short sausage, selected from the best part of the exploited heap; in the dish thus provided they contrive a hatching-chamber, in which the egg is daintily lodged. Thanks to the mother's care, often, also, to the father's, the new-born grub finds itself provided with all it could wish. It is a privileged creature, spared the asperities of life.

The Trox, on the other hand, has a harsh and pitiless training. The grub has to find board and lodging at its own cost and peril, a serious question even for a consumer of Fox-dung. The mother scatters her eggs

[1] For the Scarabæus, or Sacred Beetle, the Broad-necked Scarab, the Spanish Copris and the Lunary Copris, cf. *The Sacred Beetle and Others:* chaps. i to x. and xvi.—*Translator's Note.*

[2] Cf. *The Sacred Beetle and Others:* chaps. xi., xvii. and xviii.—*Translator's Note.*

under the furry ordure. Her foresight in
the interest of her young goes no further.
The cake that nourishes her will feed her
family likewise. It is large and will be
enough for all.

In order to follow the first actions of the
grubs, I set apart a few eggs, singly, in a
glass tube. At the bottom is a column of
moist sand; above this is a store of food
taken from that part of the Vulpine excre-
ment which is richest in Rabbit's fur.
Hatched by day, the grub at first attends to
its lodging. It digs, hollowing itself a retreat in the sand, a short, vertical shaft into
which a few scraps of the fostering felt are
dragged afterwards. As and when the provisions are consumed, the grub returns to the
surface to collect more.

The manœuvres of the grubs in the chief
establishment, the earthenware pan with the
wire-gauze cover, begin and are continued in
the same fashion. Under cover of the heap
exploited in common, the larvæ have dug
themselves a vertical shaft apiece, the length
of a man's finger and the diameter of a thick
pencil. At the bottom of the dwelling there
is no mass of victuals stored up in advance,
such as the abundance on the surface would

permit. Instead of hoarding, the Trox-larvæ live from day to day, I surprise them, above all in the evening, discreetly climbing to the top, scraping the heap above their pit, collecting a shaggy armful and immediately climbing down again tail foremost. They do not reappear so long as the little bale of fur holds out. When their provisions are finished and their appetite returns, they make a fresh ascent and a fresh collection.

This frequent coming and going in the shaft threatens sooner or later to bring down the sandy wall. Here we see renewed the industry of the Geotrupes couples, who have a way of plastering the wall of their pit with dung in order to avoid its collapsing while the material of the huge sausage is being amassed on repeated journeys; only, with the Trox, it is the larva itself that undertakes the work of consolidation. From end to end it lines its gallery with the same felt on which it feeds.

In three or four weeks' time, all the hairy materials of the heap have disappeared underground, dragged by the larvæ to the bottom of their burrows. On the surface of the soil nothing is left except the remains of the bones. The adults have gone to earth and are dead or dying. Their time is over. I obtain the first nymphs at midsummer. A glass receptacle shows them to me slowly turning round and round and polishing with their backs the earthy wall of their cell, a simple, oval cavity.

By the middle of July the perfect insect has matured. Not yet defiled by the dirt of its calling, it is really magnificent in its ebony cuirass, its strings of large beads surmounted by white hairs, its hinder and middle tarsi shod with bright red. It comes up to the surface, finds the Fox's dejecta, settles down and from now onward is a filthy scavenger. Once torpid in the sand, under the heap of ordure which serves it as a roof, it will pass the winter there and resume its labours in the spring.

When all is said, the Trox is a somewhat uninteresting insect. One single point in her history deserves to be remembered, namely, her predilection for what the Fox's stomach has refused. I know another instance of these peculiar tastes. The Owl, when he has caught a Field-mouse, stuns her with a blow of his beak on the back of the neck and swallows her whole. It is for the

digestive pouch to bone and skin her and
sift the bad from the good. When the selection is made—as it is, most admirably—
the bird, with a shrug of its body, gets rid
of the indigestible stuff; it vomits a pellet of
bones and fur. Now, just like the furry
mass evacuated by the Fox, these balls of
filth have their votaries. I have just seen
one of them at work. This is the *Choleva
tristis*, PANZ., a dwarf related to the family
of the Silphæ.

Is the fur of a Rabbit or a Field-mouse
such a very precious thing, then, that it has
special exploiters appointed to work at it
again after the Fox's intestine and the Owl's
crop have been unable to break it up and
use it? Yes, this fur has a certain value.
Nature's treasury claims it for fresh purposes with such an imperious voice that our
own industries, which in their fashion are
endowed with a terrific power, of digestion,
cannot guarantee us the protracted possession of what was a scrap of fluff.

Cloth comes from the Sheep. It has been
worked up by the teeth of machinery at the
spinner's and the weaver's; it has been
steeped in chemicals at the dyer's; it has
passed through worse ordeals than an at-

tempt to digest it. Is it now safe from attack? No: the Moth vie with us for its possession.

Poor swallow-tail coat of mine, of supple broadcloth, companion of my drudgery [1] and witness of my poverty, I abandon you without regret for the peasant's jacket; you are reposing in a drawer, with a few bags of camphorated lavender; the housewife keeps an eye on you and shakes you from time to time. Useless pains! You will perish by the Clothes-moths, as the Mole perished by the maggot, the Snake by the Dermestes and we ourselves by. . . . Let us not dig that last pit of all before the hour has struck. Everything must return to the renovating crucible into which death is continually pouring materials to ensure the continual blossoming of life.

---

[1] This is a reference to the days when the author was a provincial schoolmaster. Cf. *The Life of the Fly:* chaps. xiii., xiv., xix., and xx.—*Translator's Note.*

CHAPTER IV

MINOTAURUS TYPHŒUS : THE BURROW

TO describe the insect which forms the subject of this chapter, scientific nomenclature has combined two formidable names: that of the Minotaur, Minos' Bull fed on human flesh in the windings of the Cretan labyrinth, and that of Typhon or Typhœus, one of the giants, sons of Terra, who attempted to scale heaven. Thanks to the clue of thread which he received from Minos' daughter Ariadne, Theseus the Athenian found the Minotaur, slew him, and came out safe and sound, after delivering his country for ever from the dreadful tribute destined for the monster's food.

Typhœus, struck by a thunder-bolt on his piled-up mountains, was hurled into the flanks of Etna. He is still there. His breath is the smoke of the volcano. When he coughs, he spews forth streams of lava; when he shifts his weight from shoulder to shoulder, he puts all Sicily in a flutter: he shakes her with an earthquake.

It is not unpleasing to find an echo of these old fables in natural history. Mythological names, so resonant and grateful to the ear, do not entail any contradiction with reality, a defect not always avoided by terms entirely built up of data derived from the lexicon. When, moreover, vague analogies connect the fabulous with the historical, then the happiest surnames and forenames are obtained. *Minotaurus Typhœus* LIN. is an instance in point. It is the name given to a fair-sized black Beetle, closely related to the earth-borers, the Geotrupes.[1] This is a peaceable, inoffensive creature, but even better provided with horns than Minos' Bull. None among our armour-loving insects wears so threatening a panoply. The male carries on his corselet a bundle of three sharp spears, parallel and pointed forwards. Imagine him the size of a Bull: Theseus himself, if he met him in the fields, would not dare to face his terrible trident.

The Typhœus of the legend had the ambition to sack the home of the gods by stack-

[1] The Beetle under consideration is known to some nomenclators as Geotrupes Typhœus.—*Translator's Note.*

ing one atop of the other a pile of mountains wrenched from their base; the Typhœus of the naturalists does not climb: he descends; he bores the soil to enormous depths. The first, with a heave of the shoulder, set a province trembling; the second, with a thrust of his back, makes his little mound quake as Etna quakes when he who lies buried beneath her stirs.

Such is the insect which I propose to study to-day, penetrating as far as may be into the secret sources of its actions. The few particulars which I have already gained, during the long period of my acquaintance with it, make me suspect habits worthy of a fuller record.

But what is the use of this record, what the use of all this minute research? I well know that it will not bring about a fall in the price of pepper, a rise in that of crates of rotten cabbages or other serious events of this sort, which cause fleets to be manned and set people face to face intent upon exterminating one another. The insect does not aspire to so much glory. It confines itself to showing us life in all the inexhaustible variety of its manifestations; it helps us to decipher in some small measure the obscurest book of all, the book of ourselves.

Insects are easy to obtain, by no means burdensome to feed and not repulsive when subjected to a physical examination; and they lend themselves far better than the higher animals to our curious investigations. Besides, the others are our near kinsfolk and do but repeat a somewhat monotonous theme, whereas insects, with their unparalleled wealth of instincts, habits and structure, reveal a new world to us, much as though we were conferring with the natives of another planet. This is why I hold insects in such high esteem and constantly renew my untiring relations with them.

Minotaurus Typhœus affects the open sandy places where the flocks of Sheep, on their way to the pasture, scatter their trails of black pellets, which constitute his daily food. In their absence, he also accepts the tiny products of the Rabbit, which are easy to gather, for the timid rodent, perhaps afraid of scattering broadcast the evidences of his whereabouts, always goes to some accustomed spot surrounded by tufts of thyme, to deposit his droppings.

These to the Minotaur represent victuals of inferior quality, utilized, in the absence of anything better, for his own nourishment, but not served to his family. He prefers those supplied by the flock. Were it a matter of naming him according to his tastes, we should have to call him the assiduous collector of Sheep-droppings. This pastoral predilection did not escape the old observers, one of whom speaks of him as the Sheep Scarab, *Scarabæus ovinus*.

The burrows, which may be recognized by the little mound that surmounts them first become numerous in autumn, when the rains have at last come to moisten the soil parched by the scorching heat of summer. Then the young of this year emerge slowly from underground and for the first time come out to enjoy the light; then, for a few weeks, they feast in temporary marquees; and next they begin to hoard with a view to the winter.

Let us inspect the dwelling: an easy task, for which a simple pocket-trowel will suffice. The mansion occupied in the late autumn is a shaft as wide as a man's finger and about nine inches deep. There is no special chamber, but a sunk pit, as perpendicular as the

inequalities of the soil will allow it to be.
The owner, now of one sex, now of the other,
is at the bottom, always alone. The time
to settle down and establish a family not
having yet arrived, each of them lives like
an anchorite and thinks only of his own welfare. Above the hermit a vertical column
of Sheep-droppings blocks the dwelling.
There is often enough to fill the palm of
one's hand.

How did the Minotaur acquire so much
wealth? He amasses it easily, being spared
the worry of seeking it, for he is always
careful to install himself near a copious def-
ecation. He gleans on the very threshold
of his door. When he thinks fit, especially
at night, he chooses from the heap of pellets
one to suit him. Using his clypeus as a lever, he loosens it below; rolling it gently,
he brings it to the orifice of the pit, where
the booty is swallowed up. More follow,
one by one, all easily handled because of
the olive-like shape. They roll like casks
trundled by the cooper.

When the Sacred Beetle proposes to go
banqueting underground far from the mad-
ding crowd, he packs his share of victuals
into a ball; he gives it its spherical form,

that best adapted to transport. The Minotaur, though also versed in the mechanics of
rolling, has no occasion to make these preparations: the Sheep saves him the trouble by
modelling fragments which are easily moved.

At last, satisfied with his harvest, the
gleaner goes indoors. What will he do
with his treasure? Feed on it, that goes
without saying, until the cold and its con-
sequent torpor stay the appetite. But eating is not everything. In the winter, certain
precautions become essential in a retreat of
only middling depth. When December
draws nigh, already we find a few mounds
as large as those of spring. They correspond with burrows running down three feet
or more. In these deeply buried crypts
there is always a female who, sheltered from
the rough weather outside, is frugally nibbling at her scanty provender.

Dwellings like these, with an equable
temperature, are still rare. The majority,
always occupied by a single inhabitant,
whether male or female, are barely nine
inches deep. As a rule, they are padded
with a thick blanket, obtained from dry pellets, crumbled and reduced to shreds. We
may take it that this fibrous mass, which is

eminently fitted to retain the heat, has a good deal to do with the hermit's comfort in severe weather. In the late autumn, the Minotaur hoards so that he may take refuge in a felt mattress when the cold really sets in.

Couples addicted to nest-building in concert begin to meet in the early days of March. The two sexes, hitherto isolated in burrows near the surface, are now associated for a long time to come. Where does the meeting take place, where is the agreement to collaborate concluded? One fact, to begin with, attracts my attention. At the end of autumn, as in winter, females abound as frequently as the males. When March comes, I find hardly any, so much so that I despair of properly stocking the cage in which I propose to observe the insects' habits. To fifteen males I unearth three females at most. What has become of the latter, so numerous in the beginning?

True, I am excavating the burrows most readily accessible to my pocket-trowel. Perhaps the secret of the absentees lies at the bottom of those retreats which are more difficult to inspect. Let us appeal to arms, suppler and stronger than my own; let us take a spade and dig deep into the soil. I am rewarded for my perseverance; Females are found at last, as many as I could wish. They are alone, without provisions, at the bottom of a perpendicular gallery whose depth would discourage any one not endowed with exemplary patience.

Everything is now explained. From the time of the spring awakening and even sometimes at the end of autumn, before they have made the acquaintance of their collaborators, the valiant future mothers set to work, choosing a good place and sinking a shaft which, if it does not yet attain the requisite depth, will at least be the starting-point of more considerable works. It is in these shafts, more or less advanced, that the suitors come in search of the workers, at the secret hours of the twilight. Sometimes there are several of them. It is not uncommon to find two or three gathered round the same bride. As one is enough, the others decamp and pursue their quest elsewhere, as soon as the lady's choice and perhaps a bit of a skirmish have concluded the matter.

The quarrels among these pacific creatures cannot be very serious. A little grappling with the legs, whose toothed shanks grate upon the rigid harness; a few tumbles provoked by blows of the trident: the strife amounts to no more than this. When the superfluous wooers are gone, the pairing takes place, the household is established; and then and there bonds are contracted which are remarkably enduring.

Are these bonds never dissolved? Do the husband and wife recognize each other among their fellows? Are they mutually faithful? Cases of connubial disloyalty are very rare, are in fact unknown, on the part of the mother, who has long ceased to leave the house; on the other hand, they are frequent on the part of the father, whose duties often compel him to go abroad. As we shall see presently, he is throughout his life the purveyor of victuals, the person appointed to cart away the rubbish. Single-handed, at different hours of the day, he shoots out of doors the earth thrown up by the mother's excavations; single-handed he explores the surroundings of the house at night, in quest of pellets whereof to knead the children's loaves.

Sometimes two burrows are side by side. May not the collector of provisions, on returning home, easily mistake the door and

enter another's house? On his walks
abroad, does he never happen to meet ladies
taking the air who have not yet settled down
and then, forgetful of his first mate, does
he not qualify for divorce? The question
was worth looking into. I have tried to
solve it in the following manner.

I take two couples from the ground when
the excavations are in full swing. Indelible
marks, scratched with a needle on the lower
edge of the wing-cases, will enable me to distinguish them one from the other. The
four objects of my experiment are distributed at random, singly, over the surface of
a sandy space some eighteen inches deep.
Soil of this depth will be sufficient for the
excavations of a night. In case provisions
should be needed, I supply a handful of
Sheep-droppings. A large earthenware pan,
turned upside down, covers the arena, prevents escape and affords the darkness favourable to peaceful concentration.

Next day, I obtain splendid results.
There are two burrows in the settlement and
no more; the couples have formed again as
they were: each Jack has recovered his Jill.
A second experiment, made next day, and
yet a third meet with the same success: the

marked couples are together, those not marked are together, at the bottom of the shaft.

Five times more, day after day, I make them set up house anew. Things now begin to go amiss. Sometimes each of my four subjects settles down apart from the rest; sometimes the same burrow contains the two males or the two females; sometimes the same vault receives the two sexes, but associated otherwise than in the beginning. I have repeated the experiment too often. Henceforth, disorder reigns. My daily shufflings have demoralized the diggers; a crumbling house that has constantly to be begun afresh has put an end to lawful unions. Respectable married life becomes impossible from the moment when the house falls in from day to day.

No matter: the first three experiments, made when scares, time after time renewed, had not yet tangled the delicate connecting thread, seem to point to a certain constancy in the Minotaur's household. The male and female recognize each other, find each other in the confusion of events which my mischievous doings force upon them; they exhibit a mutual fidelity, a very unusual quality in the insect class, which is but too prone to forget its matrimonial obligations.

How do they recognize each other? We recognize one another by our facial features, which vary so greatly in different individuals, notwithstanding their common likeness. They, to tell the truth, have no faces; there is no expression beneath their rigid masks. Besides, things happen in profound darkness. The sense of sight therefore does not count at all.

We recognize one another by our speech, by the tone, the inflection of our voices. They are dumb, deprived of all means of vocal appeal. There remains the sense of smell. *Minotaurus* finding his mate makes me think of my friend Tom, the house-dog, who, when the moon stirs his emotions, lifts his nose in the air, sniffs the breeze and jumps the garden-walls, eager to obey the remote and magical summons; he puts me in mind of the Great Peacock Moth,[1] who hastens from miles afield to pay his respects to the newly-hatched maid.

The comparison, however, is far from being complete, the Dog and the big Moth

[1] Cf. *The Life of the Caterpillar,* by J. Henri Fabre, translated by Alexander Teixeira de Mattos: chap. xi.— *Translator's Note.*

get wind of the wedding before they know the bride. The Minotaur, on the contrary, has no experience of long pilgrimages and makes his way, within a short radius, to her whom he has already frequented; he recognizes her, he distinguishes her from the others by certain emanations, certain individual secrets inappreciable to any save the enamoured swain. Of what do these effluvia consist? The insect did not tell me; and that is a pity, for it might have taught us things worth knowing about its powers of smell.

Now how is the work divided in this household? To discover this is no easy undertaking, for which the point of a penknife will suffice. He who proposes to inspect the burrowing insect in its home must resort to exhausting excavations. We have not here the chamber of the Sacred Beetle, the Copris or other Beetles, which is uncovered without trouble with a mere pocket-trowel; we have a shaft whose floor can be reached only with a stout spade, manfully wielded for hours at a stretch. And, if the sun be at all hot, you return from your drudgery, feeling utterly worn out.

Oh, my poor joints, grown rusty with age!

More Beetles

To suspect the existence of a beautiful problem underground and to be unable to dig! The zeal survives, as ardent as in the days when I used to demolish the spongy slopes beloved of the Anthophoræ;[1] the love of research has not abated; but my strength fails me. Fortunately I have an assistant in the person of my son Paul, who lends me the vigour of his wrists and the suppleness of his back. I am the head, he is the arm.

The rest of the family, including the mother—and she not the least eager—usually go with us. You cannot employ too many eyes when the pit becomes deep and you have to observe from a distance the tiny objects unearthed by the spade. What one overlooks another will detect. Huber,[2] when he was blind, studied the Bees through the intermediary of a clear-sighted and devoted helper. I am even better off than the great Swiss naturalist. My sight, which is still fairly good though much worn, is as-

[1] A genus of wild Bees. Cf. *Bramble-bees and Others,* by J. Henri Fabre, translated by Alexander Teixeira de Mattos: chaps. iv. and vii. and *passim.—Translator's Note.*

[2] François Huber (1750-1831), the Swiss naturalist, author of *Nouvelles Observations sur les Abeilles.* He early became blind from excessive study and thereafter conducted his scientific work with the aid of his wife.— *Translator's Note.*

sisted by the perspicacious eyes of all my family. I owe it to them that I am able to continue my research-work: let me thank them here and now.

We are on the spot early in the morning. We find a burrow with a large mound formed of cylindrical plugs forced out as though by blows of the hammer. We clear away this hillock and a pit opens below it. A good, long reed, gathered on the way, is inserted in the hole. Pushed farther home, as the surface soil is cleared away, it will serve us as a guide.

The soil is quite loose, unmixed with pebbles, which are obnoxious to the digging insect that loves the perpendicular and especially obnoxious to the cutting edge of the exploring spade. It consists solely of sand cemented with a little clay. The digging would therefore be easy, if one had not to reach depths in which tools become extremely difficult to handle unless the whole area is overturned. The following method gives good results without unduly increasing the volume of earth removed, a procedure to which the owner might object.

A space of roughly a yard in radius is attacked around the shaft. As the guiding

reed is laid bare, we push it lower in. It
began by going about nine inches underground, it is now eighteen inches down.
Soon it becomes impracticable to remove the
earth with the spade, which is hampered by
lack of room. We have to go on our knees,
collect the rubbish in both hands and toss it
outside. The more we do so, the deeper
the hole becomes, increasing the already
enormous difficulty. A moment arrives
when, to continue, we are obliged to lie flat
on our stomachs and dip the front of our
bodies into the hole, as far as our more or
less supple waists allow. Each dip flings up
a good handful of earth. And the reed
goes lower and lower, without giving any
indication of an immediate check.

It is impossible for my son to continue in
this fashion, despite his youthful elasticity.
To reach the bottom of the disheartening
cavity, he lowers the level of the sustaining
soil. A cut is made at one side of the circular pit, giving just enough space to admit his
two knees. This is a shelf, a ledge, which
will be lowered as we go on. The work is
resumed, this time more actively; but the
reed, when we consult it, descends, descends
to a great depth.

The Burrow

We lower the supporting shelf still more and employ the spade again. When the rubbish is removed, the excavation is more than three feet deep. Are we there at last? Not at all: the terrible reed dives still lower down. Let us sink the ledge again and continue. Perseverance is rewarded. At four feet and a half, the reed touches the obstacle; it goes no farther. Victory! The task is done: we have reached the Minotaur's chamber.

The pocket-trowel discreetly lays it bare and the occupants appear: first the male, and, a little lower down, the female. When the couple are removed, a dark, circular patch is seen: this is the top of the column of provisions. Let us be careful: dig gently! What we have to do is to cut away the central clod at the bottom of the pit, to separate it from the surrounding earth and then, slipping the trowel underneath and using it as a lever, to extract the block all in a lump. There! That's done! We have the couple and their nest. A morning of arduous digging has procured us these treasures: Paul's broiling back can tell us at the cost of what efforts.

This depth of nearly five feet is not and

could not be uniform: there are many causes that induce it to vary, such as the degree of moisture and consistency in the soil traversed, the insect's passion for work and the time available, according to the more or less remote date of the egg-laying. I have seen burrows dip a little deeper; I have seen others reach not quite three feet. In any case, *Minotaurus*, to settle his family, requires a lodging of extravagant depth, such as is dug by no other burrower of my acquaintance. Presently we shall have to ask ourselves what imperious needs oblige the collector of Sheep-droppings to dwell at such depths.

Before leaving the spot, let us note a fact whose evidence will be of value later. The female was right at the bottom of the burrow; above her, at some distance, was the male: both were struck motionless with fright in the midst of an occupation whose nature we are as yet hardly able to specify. This detail, observed repeatedly in the different burrows dug up, seems to show that each of the two fellow-workers has a definite place.

The mother, more skilled in nursery matters, occupies the lower floor. She alone digs, versed as she is in the properties of the perpendicular, which economizes labour while giving the greatest depth. She is the engineer, always in touch with the working-face of the shaft. The other is her labourer. He is stationed in the rear, ready to load the rubbish on his horny hod. Later, the excavatrix becomes a baker: she kneads the cakes for the children into cylinders; the father is then the baker's boy. He brings her from outside the wherewithal for making flour. As in every well-regulated household, the mother is minister of the interior, the father minister of the exterior. This would explain the invariable position in their cylindrical home. The future will tell us if these conjectures truly correspond with the reality.

For the moment, let us examine at our leisure, in the comfort of our own home, the central clod, so laboriously acquired. It contains a preserved foodstuff in the shape of a sausage nearly as long and as thick as a man's finger. This is composed of a dark, compact material, arranged in layers, which we recognize as the Sheep-pellets reduced to small crumbs. Sometimes the dough is fine and almost homogeneous from one end of the cylinder to the other; more often the piece is a sort of hardbake, in which large fragments are held together by an amalgamation of cement. The baker apparently varies the more or less careful composition of her confectionery according to the time at her disposal.

The stuff is tightly packed into the closed end of the burrow, where the walls are smoother and more elaborately treated than in the rest of the shaft. The point of the knife easily rids it of the surrounding earth, which peels off like a rind. In this way I obtain the food-cylinder free from any earthy stain.

When this is done, let us enquire into the matter of the egg, for this pastry has certainly been manipulated for the sake of a grub. Guided by what I learnt in the old days from the Geotrupes, who lodge the egg at the lower end of their black-pudding, in a special recess contrived in the very heart of the provisions, I look to find the egg of the Minotaur, their near kinsmen, in a hatching-chamber right at the bottom of the sausage. I am mistaken. The egg sought for is not at the spot anticipated, nor at the other end, nor in any part whatsoever of the victuals.

A search outside the provisions reveals it me at last. It is below the food, in the sand itself, and has benefited by none of the meticulous cares wherein mothers excel. There is here not a smooth-walled chamber, such as the delicate skin of the new-born larva would seem to demand, but a rough, irregular cavity, the result of a mere falling in rather than of material ingenuity. The grub is to be hatched in this rude crib, at some distance from its provisions. To reach the food, it will have to demolish and pass through a ceiling of sand some millimetres thick. As regards her offspring, the Minotaur mother is an expert in the art of sausage-making, but she knows nothing at all of the endearments of the cradle.

Anxious to watch the hatching and observe the growth of the larva, I install my find in cells reproducing as nearly as may be the natural conditions. A glass tube closed at one end of the same diameter as the burrow receives first a bed of moist sand to represent the original soil. On the surface of this layer I place the egg. A little of the same sand forms the ceiling through which the new-born grub must pass to reach the provisions. There are none other than the regulation sausage, rid of its earthy rind. A few careful strokes of the rammer make it occupy the available space. Lastly, a plug of wet, but not dripping cotton-wool fills up the cell completely. This will be a source of permanent moisture, similar to that of the depths in which the mother establishes her family. The provisions will thus remain soft, in accordance with the youthful consumer's needs.

This softness of the food and the flavour produced by the fermentation due to moisture probably have somthing to say to the instinct to bore deeply at the time of egg-laying. What do the father and mother really want? Do they dig to ensure their own welfare? Do they go so low down in order to find an agreeable temperature and moisture when the fierce summer heat prevails? Not at all. Endowed with a robust constitution and loving the sun's kisses as other insects do, they both inhabit, until the family is founded, a modest dwelling in a convenient position. Not even the inclemencies of winter drive them to seek a better shelter.

The Burrow

At nesting-time it is another matter.
They descend to a great depth underground.
Why? Because their family, which is
hatched about June, must find soft food
awaiting it at a time when the heat of summer will bake the soil hard as a brick. The
tiny sausage, if it lay at a depth of ten or
twenty inches, would become hard as horn
and uneatable; and the grub, incapable of biting into the tough ration, would perish. It is
important therefore that the victuals should
be cellared at a depth where the most violent
heat of the sun cannot lead to desiccation.

Many other food-packers know the risks
of excessive dryness. Each has his own
method of warding off the danger. The
Geotrupes makes his home under the volu-
minous heap dropped by the Mule, an excellent obstacle to speedy desiccation. Besides,
he works in autumn, the season of frequent
showers; moreover, he gives his product the
shape of a big roly-poly, of which the middle
part, the only part used, gives up its moisture very slowly. For these several reasons,
he digs burrows of medium depth.

The Sacred Beetle likewise attaches no
value to remote retreats. He houses his offspring in vaults at no great distance from the

surface of the soil; but he makes amends by
fashioning the victuals into a ball: he knows
that round tins keep their contents moist.
The Copris does very much the same with his
ovoids. So with the others, the Sisyphus,[1]
the Gymnopleurus.[2] The Minotaur alone
takes an enormous dive underground.

There are different reasons that call for
this. Here is a second, more imperious even
than the first. The dung-workers all go for
recent materials, fully endowed with their
toothsome and plastic qualities. To this
system of baking the Minotaur makes a
stronger exception: what he needs is old, dry,
arid stuff. I have never seen him, either in
my cages or in the open country, gather pellets quite recently ejected. He wants them
dried by long exposure to the sun's rays.

But, to suit the grub, the hard food has
to simmer for a long time and to improve
by keeping, in surroundings saturated with
moisture. So the coarse whole-meal bread
is replaced by the bun. The laboratory in
which the children's food is prepared must
therefore be a very deep-seated factory,
which can never be entered by the drought

[1] *The Sacred Beetle and Others:* chap. x., Cf. v—
Translator's Note.
[2] Cf. *idem*, chap. viii.—*Translator's Note.*

of summer however long prolonged. Here succulence and flavour are imparted to dry materials which no other member of the stercoral guild thinks of employing, for lack of an annealing-chamber, of which *Minotaurus* possesses the monopoly. And, the better to fulfil his mission in life, he also possesses an instinct to bore to enormous depths. The nature of the victuals makes an incomparable well-sinker of the three-pronged Dung-beetle; his talents have been determined by a hard crust.

CHAPTER V

LONG ago, the Minotaur's cousins, the
Geotrupes, afforded me a delightfully
unusual spectacle, that of a prolonged associ-
ation in pairs, a real domestic couple, working in common for the children's welfare.
Philemon and Baucis, as I used to call them,
prepared their board and lodging with equal
ardour. Philemon, the sturdier of the two,
compressed the food by pushing it with his
fore-arms; Baucis explored the heap on the
surface, picking out the best part and lower-
ing by the armful the wherewithal to manufacture the enormous sausage. It was magnificent to see the mother sifting and the
father compressing.

A cloud overshadowed this exquisite picture. My subjects occupied a cage wherein
any inspection demanded an excavation on
my part, discreetly conducted, it is true, but
enough to startle the labourers and make

them stop work. With unsparing patience, I thus obtained a series of snapshots which the logic of things, that delicate cinematographer, afterwards combined to form a living scene. I wished for more than this: I should have liked to observe the couple in continuous action, from the beginning to the end of their task. I had to abandon the idea, so impossible did it seem to me to observe the mysterious underground happenings without perturbing excavations.

To-day, my ambition to achieve the impossible has returned. The Minotaur proclaims himself a rival of the Geotrupes; he even appears to be their superior. I propose to follow his actions underground, at a depth of a yard and more, completely at my ease, without in any way distracting the insect from its occupations. To do this I shall need the eyes of a Lynx, which are said to be capable of piercing the opaquest night, whereas I have only my ingenuity to fall back upon in endeavouring to see plainly in the dark. Let us see what it can do.

To begin with, the direction of the burrow enables me to foresee that my plan is not altogether absurd. When digging her nest, the Minotaur descends perpendicularly. If she worked at random, following all sorts of directions, excavation would demand an infinite area of soil, out of all proportion to the means at my disposal. Well, her invariable adherence to the perpendicular informs me that I need not trouble about the quantity of sand available, but only about the depth of the bed. In these conditions, the undertaking is not unreasonable.

As good luck will have it, I possess a glass tube which has long been diverted from chemistry and placed at the service of entomology. It is a yard or more in length, and over an inch in width. If fixed in a vertical position, it will do, I think, for the Minotaur's shaft. I close one end with a plug and fill the tube with a mixture of fine sand and moist clay soil, packing the mixture in layers with a ramrod. This column will be the plot of ground allotted to the digger to work in.

But it must be kept upright and completed with different accessories essential to successful operation. For this purpose, three bamboo canes are planted in the earth contained in a large flower-pot. Joined at their tips, they form a tripod, a frame supporting the whole structure. The tube is set up in the

centre of the triangular base. A small
earthenware pie-dish with a hole made in
the bottom, receives the open upper end,
which projects a little and holds a layer of
earth that comes level with the brim. This
will represent, around the mouth of the
shaft, the space in which the insect can attend
to its business, either to shoot the rubbish
from the shaft or to gather the provisions
round about. Lastly, a glass bell, fitting
into the dish, prevents escape and preserves
the slight quantity of moisture needed. A
few supporting strings and bits of wire keep
the whole thing firmly fixed.

We must not overlook one most important detail. The diameter of the tube is
about twice that of the natural burrow.
Therefore, if the insect digs along the axis
and in an exactly perpendicular direction, it
will have at its disposal more than the required width. It will obtain a channel lined
on every side by a wall of sand a few millimetres thick. We may however assume
that the digger, knowing nothing of geometrical precision and ignorant of the conditions provided for it, will take no account
of the axis and will deviate from it to one
side or the other. Moreover, the least ad-

ditional resistance in the substance traversed will cause the Beetle to turn aside slightly, now hither, now thither. Consequently the glass wall will be completely denuded at sundry points; windows will be formed, chinks upon which I rely to make observation possible, but which will be hateful to the darkness-loving workers.

To make sure of these windows and save the insect from them, I sheath the tube in a few cardboard sheaths which can be gently slipped up and down and which fit inside one another. With this arrangement, I shall be able, when required, and without distracting the insect from its work, to create alternately, by a simple movement of the thumb, a little light for myself and darkness for the Beetle. The distribution of the movable sheaths, which slip up or down as needed, will allow the tube to be examined from end to end as and when the accidents of boring open up new windows.

A last precaution is necessary. If I merely put the couple simply in the dish surmounted by the bell-glass, it is probable that the prisoners will not realize what a small portion of the soil is available for digging. It will be best for me to teach them the right spot in the centre of an impregnable area. For this purpose, I leave the top of the tube empty to a depth of a few fingers'-breadths; and, as a glass wall would be impossible to climb, I provide this part with a lift, that is to say, I line it with wiregauze. When this is done, the two insects, male and female, unearthed together from their natural burrow, are inserted into this entrance-hall, where they will find their familiar environment, the sandy soil. With a little food scattered about the pit, it will be enough, I hope, to make them like their peculiar lodging.

What results shall I obtain with my rustic apparatus, so long planned by the fireside during the winter evenings? Certainly it is not much to look at; it would gain a poor reception in the laboratories that are constantly perfecting their equipment. It is peasant's work, a clumsy combination of common objects. I agree; but let us remember that, in the pursuit of truth, the poor and simple are by no means inferior to the most magnificent. My arrangement of three bamboo canes has given me delight-

ful moments; it has provided me with some
fascinating glimpses which I will try to set
forth.

In March, at the time of the great nest-
building excavations, I dig up a couple in
the fields. I install them in my apparatus.
In case provisions should be needed as a re-
storative during the laborious sinking of the
shaft, I place a few Sheep-droppings under
the glass bell, near the mouth of the tube.
The trick of the empty entrance-hall, calcu-
lated to bring the prisoners into immediate
touch with the workable column of earth,
succeeds to perfection. Soon after their installation, the captives have recovered from
their excitement and are diligently at work.

They were taken from their home in the
full ardour of excavation and they continue
in my garden the task which I interrupted.
It is true that I changed the site of their
workshop as quickly as I could return from
their place of origin, which was not far away.
Their zeal has not had time to grow cold.
They were digging just before removal and
they continue to dig. Time is pressing; the
pair will not willingly down tools, even after
an upheaval which one would think must
have demoralized them.

First Attempts at Observation

As I anticipated, the digging assumes an eccentric direction, producing in the sandy wall a few gaps in which the glass is laid bare. These peep-holes are none too satisfactory as regards my plans; while some of them permit of clear observation, the greater number are obscured by an earthy veil. Besides, they are not permanent. New ones open daily, while others close. These continual variations are due to the rubbish which, laboriously hoisted outside, rubs against the wall, plastering or denuding this point or that. I take advantage of these fortuitous openings to examine as best I may, when the light falls at a favourable angle, the interesting things happening inside the tube.

I see over and over again, at my leisure, as often as I please and over a protracted period, what the exhausting inspection of the natural burrows showed me in rare and fleeting glimpses. The mother is always ahead, in the post of honour, at the working-face. Alone she toils and moils, with her clypeus; alone she scrapes and digs, with the harrow of her toothed arms: her mate never relieves her. The father is always in the rear, very busy too, but on another job. His task it is to carry the loosened soil outside and to clear up as the pioneer goes deeper and deeper.

This labour of his is no slight affair, as we may judge from the mound which he throws up when plying his trade in the meadows. It is a big heap of earthen plugs, of cylinders mostly measuring an inch in length. You need only examine the pieces to see that the navvy handles blocks of Cyclopean dimensions. He does not carry off the excavated soil fragment by fragment; he ejects it in huge agglomerations.

What should we think of a miner who was obliged to hoist to the surface, to a height of some hundreds of feet, an overpoweringly heavy hod of coal up a narrow, perpendicular shaft which could be climbed only by the use of his knees and elbows? The Minotaur father's ordinary task is the equivalent of this feat of strength. He performs it with great dexterity. How does he manage to do it? Our bamboo tripod will tell us.

From time to time, the denuded points of the tube afford me a glimpse of his doings. He is stationed at the digger's heels, raking the loosened soil towards him by the armful.

He kneads it, as its moisture enables him to do, he works it up into a plug which he thrusts back into the shaft. Then the plug begins to move. The load precedes him; and he pushes it from behind with his three-pronged fork. The work of transport would be a magnificent sight did the accidental peep-holes in the gallery lend themselves better to our curiosity. Unfortunately, they are few and small and none too clear.

Let us try to devise something better. In a dimly-lit corner of my study I hang perpendicularly a glass tube of smaller calibre than the first. I leave it as it is, unprovided with an opaque sheath. At the bottom is a nine-inch column of earth. All the rest is empty and may be easily observed, if the Minotaurs consent to work under such disadvantageous conditions. Provided that the experiment be not unduly prolonged, they do consent and very readily, so imperious is the need of a burrow as laying-time draws nigh.

I extract from the soil a couple engaged in excavating their natural shaft and place them in the glass tube. Next morning I find them continuing their interrupted business in broad daylight. Seated a little way off, in the shadow of the corner in which the apparatus hangs, I watch the operation, amazed by what I see. The mother digs. The father, at some distance, waits until the heap of rubbish is beginning to hamper the worker's movements. Then he approaches. By small armfuls he draws towards him and slips beneath his abdomen the shifted earth, which, being plastic, forms into a ball under the pressure of the hind-legs.

The Beetle now turns about beneath the load. With the trident driven into the bundle, as a pitchfork is driven into a truss of hay, before tossing it into the loft, the fore-legs, with their wide, toothed shanks, gripping the load and preventing it from crumbling, he pushes with all his might. And cheerily! The thing moves and ascends, very slowly, it is true, but still it ascends! How is it done, seeing that the too smooth surface of the glass acts as an absolute check to the upward movement?

The insurmountable difficulty has been provided for. I selected a clay soil likely to leave a trace of its passage. With the cart before the horse, the load itself sands the road and makes it practicable; in rubbing past every portion of the wall, it leaves particles of earth which constitute so many points of purchase. Therefore, as he pushes his burden upwards, the Beetle finds behind it a roughened surface which affords him. a footing as he climbs.

This, after all, is all he needs, though it involves occasional slips and efforts to retain his balance, which are unknown in the natural shaft. When he comes to a certain distance from the opening, he leaves his clod, which, shaped by the tube, remains in its place, motionless. He returns to the bottom, not by allowing himself to fall suddenly, but gradually and carefully, by means of the footholds by which he made his way up. A second pellet is hoisted up and welded to the first. A third follows. At length, with a last effort, he pushes out the whole thing in a single plug.

This fractional division is a judicious method. Because of the enormous amount of friction in the narrow and uneven natural shaft, the Beetle would never succeed in hoisting the great cylinders of his mound in one lump; he carries them up in loads which are not beyond his powers and which are afterwards joined and welded together.

More Beetles

I am inclined to believe that this work of assembling the component parts is performed in the slightly sloping vestibule which usually precedes the perpendicular shaft. Here no doubt the successive clods are compressed into one very heavy cylinder, which is yet easily moved along an almost horizontal road. Then the Minotaur, with a last thrust of his trident, pushes out the lump, which joins the others on the sides of the mound. They are like so many blocks of hewn stone forbidding access to the home. The rubbish thus suitably moulded provides a Cyclopean system of fortification.

In the glass tube, the climbing is such difficult work that the insect is soon discouraged. The frail footholds left by the load crumble and fall off, swept away by the tarsi vainly seeking a support; and the tube again becomes smooth over wide extents of its surface. The climber ends by giving up struggling against the impossible; he abandons his bundle and drops to the bottom. The works cease henceforth; the couple have recognized the treachery of their strange dwelling. Both of them try to get away. Their uneasiness is betrayed by continual attempts to escape. I set them free.

First Attempts at Observation

They have told me all that they were able to tell me in conditions so favourable to me and so bad for themselves.

To return to the large apparatus, where the work is proceeding correctly. The boring, begun in March, finishes by the middle of April. From this time onward, my daily visits no longer show me on the top of the mound a plug of fresh earth, marking a recent ejection of rubbish.

It must therefore take two or three weeks at least to excavate the dwelling. My observations in the open even lead me to think that a month or longer is not excessive. My two captives, disturbed in the midst of their earlier labours and pressed for time by the lateness of the season, cut short this work, which for that matter they were unable to continue when the cork stopper appeared at the bottom of the tube as an insuperable obstacle. The others, working in freedom, have an unlimited depth of sand at their disposal. They have plenty of leisure, if they start work in good time. Even before the end of February we see plenty of mounds. Later, these will mark the sites of shafts four or five feet deep. Such pits as these require a full month's labour, if not more.

Now what do the two well-sinkers eat, during this long period, to keep up their strength? Nothing, absolutely nothing, we are told by the two guests in my apparatus. Neither of them appears looking for food on the surface of the pie-dish. The mother does not leave the bottom for a moment; the father alone goes up and down. When he comes up, it is always with a load of rubbish. I am warned of his arrival by the hillock which shakes and partly crumbles under the impetus of the navvy and his load; but the Beetle himself does not appear, for the mouth of the erupting cone remains closed by the plug ejected. Everything happens in secret, sheltered from the indiscretion of the light. In the same way, in the fields, any burrow in process of construction remains closed until it is quite finished.

This, it is true, does not prove the absolute absence of provisions, for the father might go out at night, collect a few pellets in the neighbourhood of the shaft, push them in, go indoors again and shut up the house. In this way the couple would have enough bread in the larder to last them for a few days. This explanation must be abandoned, as we are definitely taught by what happens in my rearing-appliance.

Foreseeing a need of food, I had supplied the dish with a few droppings. When the excavation-works were finished, I found these pellets untouched and undiminished in number. The father, supposing him to go strolling about at night, could not fail to see them. He had taken no notice of them.

The peasants in my neighbourhood, rude tillers of the soil, have four meals a day. At early dawn, on rising, a hunk of bread and a few dried figs, for a snack, as they put it. In the fields, at nine o'clock, the wife brings the soup and its complement of anchovies and olives, which give a man an honest thirst. On the stroke of two, in the shade of a hedge, lunch is taken from the wallet, consisting of almonds and bread and cheese. This is followed by a sleep in the hottest part of the day. When night falls, they go home, where the housewife has made ready a salad of lettuces and a dish of fried potatoes seasoned with onions. All told, a great deal of eating to a moderate amount of work.

Ah, how greatly superior is the Minotaur!

For a month and longer, without taking any food, he works like a madman and is always fit and strong. If I told my neighbours, the chawbacons, that in a certain world the labourer does a month's hard work without a bite of food, they would reply with an incredulous guffaw. If I say as much to the chewers of ideas, perhaps I shall scandalize them.

No matter: let me repeat what the Minotaur told me. The chemical energy derived from nourishment is not the only origin of animal activity. As a source of life there is something better than digested food. What? How can I tell? Apparently the effluvia, known or unknown, emanating from the sun and transformed by the organism into a mechanical equivalent. So we were told before by the Scorpion and the Spider;[1] So we are told now by the Minotaur, who is more convincing with his arduous calling. He does not eat, yet he is a frantic worker.

The insect world is fruitful in surprises. The three-pronged Dung-beetle, an accomplished faster and nevertheless a remarkable labourer, sets us a magnificent problem. Is

[1] Cf. *The Life of the Spider:* chap. v. The essays on the Scorpion will appear in the next, the concluding volume of the series.—*Translator's Note.*

114

it not possible that on distant planets, goverened by another sun, green, blue, yellow or red, life might be exempt from the ignominy of the stomach, that lamentable source of atrocities, and maintain its activities merely with the aid of the radiations flooding that corner of the universe? Shall we ever know? I sincerely hope so, our earth being but a stage towards a better world, in which true happiness might well lie in fathoming more and more deeply the unfathomable secret of things.

Let us leave these nebulous heights and return to the workaday question of the Minotaur's affairs. The burrow is ready; it is time to establish the family. I am apprised of this by seeing the father for the first time venture abroad in the daylight. He is very busy exploring the expanse of the dish. What is he looking for? He seems to be seeking provisions for the coming brood. This is the moment to interfere.

To facilitate observation, I make a clean sweep. I clear the site of its mound, under which lie buried the victuals which I deemed necessary at the outset, but which have remained untouched. These old pellets, soiled with earth, are discarded and replaced by others, a dozen in number, distributed around the mouth of the shaft. There are, as I say, precisely twelve, arranged in groups of three, which will make it easier and quicker for me to count them daily through the haze covering the bell. A moderate watering, effected from time to time on the border of soil which surrounds the bell and keeps it in position, produces a humid atmosphere inside the apparatus similar to that of the depths favoured by the Minotaur. This element of success should not be omitted. Lastly, I keep a current account in which I enter day by day the pieces stored away. There were twelve at the beginning. If these are exhausted, we shall replace them as often as may be necessary.

I have not to wait long for the results of my preparations. That same evening, watching from a distance, I catch sight of the father leaving his home. He makes for the pellets, chooses one that suits him and, with little taps of his head, rolls it as he might roll a barrel. I steal up softly to observe the action. Forthwith the Beetle, timid to excess, abandons his morsel and dives down the shaft. The distrustful fellow has seen me; he has perceived some enormous and

116

suspicious-looking thing moving near at hand. This is more than enough to alarm him and make him postpone his harvesting. He will not reappear until perfect quiet is restored.

I now know: he who wishes to watch the gathering of the provisions must display the utmost patience and discretion. I accept the facts: I will be discreet and patient. On the following days, at different hours, I try again, silently and slyly, until success rewards me for my assiduous vigil.

Again and again I see the Minotaur go his harvesting rounds. It is always the male and the male alone that comes out and goes in quest of supplies; the mother never, never on any account, shows herself, being absorbed in other occupations at the bottom of the burrow. The provisions are transported sparingly. Down below, it seems, the culinary preparations are minute and deliberate; the housewife must be given time to work up the morsels lowered to her before we bring others which would encumber the workshop and hinder the manipulation. In ten days, beginning with the 13th of April, the date on which the male leaves home for the first time, I count twenty-three pellets stored away, say an average of a little over two in the twenty-four hours. In all, ten days' harvesting and two dozen morsels to manufacture the sausage which will form the ration of one grub.

Let us try to catch a glimpse of the couple's behaviour in private. In this connection I can have recourse to two methods, which, if employed in alternation and with perseverance, may give me the much-desired spectacle in a fragmentary form. In the first place, there is a large tripod. The narrow column of earth affords, as we know, incidental peep-holes, situated at different heights. I avail myself of these to take a glance at what happens inside. In the second place, a perpendicular, uncovered tube, the same which I used when investigating the climbing, receives a couple removed from the ground a few hours before, while actively engaged on preparing the foodstuffs.

I quite expect that my device will fail to have any lasting effect. Soon demoralized by the peculiarity of their new residence, the two insects will refuse to work, will become restless and wish to get away. No matter: before their nest-building ardour dies down, they may be able to supply me with valuable details. On combining the facts collected by means of the two methods, I obtain the following data.

The father goes out and selects a pellet whose length is greater than the diameter of the pit. He conveys it to the mouth, either backwards, by dragging it with his fore-feet, or straight ahead, by rolling it with little thrusts of his clypeus. He reaches the edge of the hole. Will he fling the lump down the precipice with one last push? Not at all: he has plans that are incompatible with a violent fall.

He enters, clasping the pellet with his legs and taking care to insert it by one end. On reaching a certain distance from the bottom, he has only to slant the piece slightly to make it find a support at its two ends against the walls of the shaft: this because of the greater length of its main axis. He thus obtains a sort of temporary flooring able to bear the load of two or three pellets. The whole forms the workshop in which the father will perform his task without disturbing the mother, who is herself engaged below. It is the mill whence will be lowered the meal for making the cakes.

The miller is well-equipped for his work.

More Beetles

Look at his trident. On the solid foundation of the corselet stand three sharp spears, the two outer ones long, the middle one short, all three pointing forwards. What purpose does this weapon serve? At first sight, one would take it for a mere masculine decoration, the corporation of Dung-beetles boasting many such, of various forms. Well, it is something more than an ornament: the Minotaur turns his gaud into a tool.

The three points of unequal length describe a concave arc, wide enough to admit a spherical dropping. Standing on his incomplete and quaking floor, which demands the employment of his four hind-legs, propped against the walls of the shaft, how will the Beetle manage to keep the slippery pellet in position and break it up? Let us watch him at work.

Stooping a little, he drives his fork into the piece, which is thenceforth rendered stationary, for it is held in the crescent-shaped jaws of the implement. The fore-legs are free; with their toothed shanks they can saw the morsel, shred it and reduce it to fragments which gradually fall through the gaps in the flooring and reach the mother below.

First Attempts at Observation

The substance which the miller shoots down is not a flour passed through the bolting-sieve, but rather a coarse meal, a mixture of pulverized remnants and of pieces hardly ground at all. Incomplete though it be, this preliminary grinding will be of the greatest assistance to the mother in her tedious job of bread-making: it will shorten the work and allow the best and the second best to be separated forthwith. When everything on the upper story, including the floor itself, is ground to powder, the horned miller returns to the open air, gathers a fresh harvest and starts his work of crumbling anew entirely at his leisure.

Nor is the baker inactive in her kitchen. She collects the remnants pouring down around her, subdivides them yet further, refines them and sorts them. This, the tenderer part, for the central crumb; that, tougher, for the crust of the loaf. Turning this way and that, she pats the material with the battledore of her flat arms; she arranges it in layers, which presently she compresses by stamping on them where they lie, much after the manner of a vintager treading his grapes. Rendered firm and compact, the mass will keep better. After some ten days of this united labour, the couple at last obtain the long, cylindrical loaf. The father has done the grinding, the mother the kneading.

On the 24th of April, everything being now in order, the male leaves the tube of my apparatus. He roams about in the bellglass, heedless of my presence, he who was at first so timid and apt to dive down the shaft at the first sight of me. He is indifferent to food. A few pellets remain on the surface. He comes upon them at every moment; he disdainfully passes them by. He has but one wish, to get away as fast as he can. This is shown by his restless marching and countermarching, by his continual attempts to scale the glass wall. He tumbles over, recovers his footing and begins all over again indefinitely, giving not a thought to the burrow, which he will never re-enter.

I let the desperate Beetle exhaust himself for twenty-four hours in vain attempts at escape. Let us come to his assistance now and restore his freedom. Or rather no, for this would mean that we should lose sight of him and remain ignorant of the object of his perturbation. I have a very large unoccupied rearing-cage. I house the

Minotaur in this cage, where he will have plenty of flying-room, choice victuals and sunlight. Next morning, in spite of all these luxuries, I find him lying on his back, with his legs stiff and stark. He is dead. The gallant fellow, having fulfilled his duties as the father of a family, felt his strength failing him; and this was the cause of his restlessness. He was anxious to go and die by himself, far away, so as not to defile the home with a corpse and trouble the widow in her subsequent operations. I admire this stoical resignation on the insect's part.

If it were an isolated, casual instance, resulting perhaps from a defective installation, there would be no reason to dwell upon the Beetle who met with his death in my apparatus. But here is something that complicates matters. In the open fields, when May is at hand, I often happen upon Minotaurs shrivelling in the sun; and these corpses are those of males, always males, with very few exceptions.

Another and a very significant detail is supplied by a cage in which I several times tried to rear the insect. As the bed of soil, some eighteen inches thick, was not deep enough, the prisoners absolutely refused to build their nests in it. Apart from this, the other, usual operations were pursued according to rule. Well, from the end of April onwards, the males ascend to the surface, one at a time. For a couple of days they wander about the trellis-work, anxious to get away. At last they tumble off, lie on their backs and slowly give up the ghost. Age has killed them.

In the first week of June, I dig up the soil in the cage from top to bottom. Of the fifteen males who were there at the beginning, hardly one remains. All have died; all the females survive. The harsh law is therefore inevitable. After helping with his hod in the lengthy task of sinking the shaft, after amassing suitable provisions and grinding the meal, the industrious trident-bearer goes away to die far from home.

CHAPTER VI

MINOTAURUS TYPHŒUS : FURTHER OBSERVATIONS

THE bamboo tripod, so alien in its arrangement to the Minotaur's habits, might well have been the cause, in part, of the father's premature decease. In the glass tube, only one cylindrical cake alone was prepared. Evidently this was not enough. Two at least are needed to maintain the species in the actual state; more would be needed, as many as possible, for increased prosperity. But in my apparatus there is no room, unless the food-cylinders are superimposed and piled in columns, a mistake which the mother would never commit.

Superimposed stories would afterwards make the emergence of the offspring difficult. In their eagerness to reach the light, the oldest, grown sufficiently mature and occupying the foot of the column, would topple over and lacerate the late arrivals, who are not yet ready to occupy the top. For a quiet exodus it is important that the shaft should be free from one end to the other. The several cavities must therefore be grouped side by side and communicate, each by a lateral passage, with the common ascension-shaft.

Long ago, the Bison Ortis [1] showed us his preserves, the rations of so many grubs, arranged near the bottom of the burrow. A short passage connected each of the chambers with the vertical shaft. The cells were all grouped on one landing. Probably the Minotaur adopts a similar system.

Indeed, when I go digging in the fields, a little late in the season, when the father is already dead, my trowel unearths a second chamber, with an egg and provisions, at some distance from the main chamber, which it-self contains an egg and is duly victualled. Another excavation gives me two eccentric cells. The arrangement is the same in each case, in the blind alley of the burrow and in its annexes: at the base, in the sand, is an egg; above it are the victuals, packed into a column.

[1] Cf. *The Sacred Beetle and Others*: chap. xvi.—*Translator's Note.*

Further Observations

It may be asssumed that, if the difficulty of wielding the spade at the bottom of a funnel had not exceeded my assistant's patience and flexibility, similar excavations, repeated throughout the proper season, would have added to the number of cells served by the same shaft. How many are there altogether? Four or five or six? I do not know exactly. A moderate number, in any case. And this is bound to be so. The hoarders of food for the family are not excessively fruitful. They have no time to bequeath supplies to a numerous brood.

The rearing-apparatus in the bamboo tripod has a surprise in store for me. I inspect it after the father's departure and decease. There is certainly a column of provisions similar to that which I dig up in the fields; but these provisions are not accompanied by an egg, either at the base or elsewhere. The table is served and the consumer is not present. Can it be that the mother is reluctant to populate the inconvenient abode which I force upon her? Apparently not, for she would not first have kneaded the long loaf, if that loaf was to have proved useless. When desisting from laying because of a defective home, she would have abstained from baking a cake that would serve no purpose.

Besides, the same fact recurs under normal conditions. In my dozen excavations in the fields—that their number was no greater must be attributed to the difficulty of the operation—the egg was lacking in three instances. The larder was deserted. No laying had taken place; and the provisions were there, manipulated in the usual fashion.

What I suspect is that the mother, not feeling in her ovaries germs ripened to the requisite degree, none the less labours to provide a store of food with her collaborator. She knows that the horned dandy, the enthusiastic helper, will disappear ere long, worn out by toil and time. She makes the most of his zeal and his energies before being deprived of them. Thus food is prepared in the cellar to be used afterwards by the mother, now a widow. To these provisions which are all the better in that they have been improved by fermentation, the mother will return, moving them and piling them up in a lateral cell, but this time with an egg under the heap. Thus provided for and enabled to carry on alone, the widow that is to be will do the rest. The father may now die; the household will not suffer unduly.

The father's premature end may well be caused by the melancholy due to inaction. He is a hard worker easily upset by the boredom of inactivity. In my apparatus, he pines away, after the first cake has been made, because the workshop is brought to a compulsory standstill, the rest of the glass having no accommodation for superimposed cells, which later would hinder the emergence of the family. For lack of space, the mother ceases to lay eggs; and the father, having nothing more to do, departs to die outside. Idleness has killed him.

In the open, the space underground is indefinite; it allows such a group of cells as is needed by the mother's fruitfulness to be formed at the bottom of the shaft; but another difficulty arises, and a most serious one. When I myself am the purveyor, there is no fear of famine. I enquire daily into the state of the stores and I renew as required the available provisions scattered over the surface. My prisoners, without being overloaded, are always in the midst of plenty. It is a very different matter in the fields.

More Beetles

The Sheep is not so lavish that she always drops at one spot the number of pellets needed by the Minotaur, two hundred and more, as my subsequent observations will testify. An emission of three or four dozen may be regarded as a good many. The ruminant moves on and continues its distribution elsewhere.

Now the pill-gatherer is not of a roaming disposition. I cannot picture him going far in quest of the wherewithal to endow his off-spring. How could he find his way again, after a long expedition, and come back home, pushing with his feet the pellets which he had picked up one by one? That flight and scent combined may enable him to light upon windfalls at a great distance for his own refection, I am quite ready to admit: the sober eater needs but little food; and, besides, the matter is not urgent. But, when nest-building is in question, the need is felt of great numbers of pellets, very quickly obtained. The Beetle, it is true, has taken care to establish himself near as copious a heap as possible. At night, he goes the rounds outside his dwelling, gathering the pellets almost on his threshold; he will even continue his search at a distance of some feet, in familiar places, where he cannot go astray. But there comes a time when nothing is left in the neighbourhood; everything has been harvested.

The hoarder, who cannot bear distant expeditions, thereupon perishes of inaction; he quits the home where henceforth there is no more work for him. Having nothing left to do for want of materials, the roller, the bruiser of pills dies out of doors, in the open air. This is my explanation of the males found dead on the surface when May comes. They are the disconsolate victims of their passion for work. They abandon life the moment life becomes useless.

If my conjecture is well-founded, it must be possible for me to prolong the existence of these pessimists by placing gradually at the workers' disposal as many pellets as they can wish for. It occurs to me to load the Minotaur with favours; I propose to create on his behalf a paradise where droppings abound, where the sugar-plums will be renewed as and when those already there are lowered into the cellar. Moreover, this delightful land will have a sandy soil, kept moist to the requisite degree; a depth equal to that of the usual burrows; and lastly ample space to allow several cabins to be grouped at the bottom, one beside the other.

My calculations result in the structure which I will now describe. With strips of boarding a good finger's-breadth thick, which will later reduce evaporation, the carpenter builds me a square, hollow prism, measuring some 56 inches in height. Three of its sides are permanently fastened with nails; the fourth consists of three shutters of equal size held in place by screws. This arrangement will enable me to inspect at will the top, the bottom or the middle part of the apparatus without shaking the contents. The inner side of the prism measures nearly 4 inches each way. The lower end is closed; the upper end is free and has a ledge on which rests a wide, projecting tray, representing the surroundings of the natural burrow. The tray is covered by a wire-gauze dome. The hollow column is filled with moist sandy earth, suitably packed. The tray itself receives a layer of the earth, a finger's-breadth in depth.

There is one indispensable condition to be observed: the earthy contents of the apparatus must not get dry. The thickness of the planks prevents this partly; but it is not enough, especially during the heat of summer. With this purpose in view, the bottom third of the long prism stands in a large flower-pot, filled with earth, which I keep damp by watering it in moderation. A slight absorption of the surrounding moisture through the wood will prevent the contents from becoming parched. The same contrivance ensures the steadiness of the apparatus, which, firmly implanted in a heavy base, will withstand the onslaughts of the wind, if need be, all the year round.

The middle third is wrapped in a thick coat of rags which the watering-can moistens almost daily. Lastly, the top third is bare; but the layer of earth on the tray, subjected by me to pretty frequent artificial rains, transmits a little moisture to it. By means of these various devices, I obtain a column of earth, neither swamped nor parched, of the kind which the Minotaur requires for his nest building.

Had I lent an ear to my ambitious plans, I should have had a dozen of these appliances constructed, so many questions were there to be solved; but it is a troublesome business, far beyond the means of my personal ingenuity; and impecuniosity, that terrible evil of which Panurge complained, curbs my desire for apparatus. I allowed myself two and no more.

When they were stocked, I kept them during the winter in a small green-house, for fear of frost in a mass of earth of no great volume. At the bottom of his natural gallery, the Minotaur need not dread the severe cold: he is protected by a wall of unlimited thickness. In the narrow quarters of my divisioning, he would have undergone the sorest trials.

When the warm weather had come, I set up my two columns in the open air, and a few steps from my door. Standing side by side, they form a sort of pylon, of a strange order of architecture. Not a member of the household passes them without a glance. My own visits are assiduous, especially in the evening and the morning, when the night work begins and when it is finished. What happy moments I have spent, on the lookout near my pylon, watching and meditating!

Here are the facts: about the middle of December, I install in each of my two appliances a female, selected from among those which best lend themselves to my designs. At this time of the year, the sexes remain

apart. The males live in burrows of middling depth; the females go down rather
lower. Some of these strenuous workers
have already, without the aid of a helper,
completed or very nearly completed the well
required for the laying. On the 10th of December, I unearth one of them at a depth of
almost four feet. These early diggers are
not what I want. Wishing to observe the
work when in full swing, I choose subjects
buried not too low down in the fields.

In the centre of the column of earth in
each apparatus, I make a shallow hole,
which marks the beginning of the burrow.
I drop the prisoner down it; and this is
enough to accustom her to the place. A re-
corded number of Sheep-droppings are distributed around the opening. Henceforth
things proceed of themselves: I have merely
to renew the provisions when the need arises.

The cold season is spent in the balmy atmosphere of a green-house; and nothing remarkable happens. A small mound is
formed, hardly big enough to fill the hollow
of my hand. The hour has not yet come for
serious operations.

In the middle of February, when the almond trees begin to blossom, the weather is

very mild. It is no longer winter, and it is not yet spring; the sun is pleasant in the daytime and at night there is a certain charm in the blaze of a few logs upon the hearth. On the rosemary bushes in the garden, already displaying their wealth of liliaceous flowers, the Bees are gathering booty, the red-bellied Osmiæ are humming, while the big grey Locusts stand twirling their great wings and proclaiming their joy of life. This delicious season of awakening spring should be to the Minotaurs' liking.

I marry my captives: I give each of them a mate, a magnificent horned male, brought home from the fields. The household is set up during the night; and without delay the couple get to work in earnest. The co-operation has given fresh life to the workshop. Before this, the males, leading solitary lives in short burrows, used commonly to doze, not caring to gather pellets or to sink shafts of any depth; the females for the most part displayed no greater industry; the burrows remained superficial, the mounds comparatively flat, the harvest unproductive. As soon as the household is established, they dig deeply, and hoard plentifully. In twice twenty-four hours, the expulsion of rubbish has hidden the home beneath a dome-shaped heap of earthly plugs nine inches in width; moreover, a dozen droppings have been sent down into the cellar.

This activity is maintained for three months or longer, broken by intervals of repose of varying duration, which are apparently rendered necessary by the operations of the miller and baker. The female never appears outside the burrow; it is always the male who emerges and sets out upon his quest, sometimes when twilight falls, more often at a later hour of the night.

The crop varies greatly, though I take care to keep the part around the burrow properly supplied. At one time, two or three pellets are enough; at another, as many as twenty are collected in a single night. The gleaner seems to be influenced by the atmospheric conditions. The harvest is usually most active when the sky looks threatening, as though preparing for a storm that fails to materialize, or when I myself create rain by watering the tray of my apparatus. In dry weather, on the contrary, whole weeks pass without the slightest attempts at storing.

As June draws nigh, feeling his end at

hand, the gallant fellow redoubles his ardour; he wishes before he dies to leave his family abundantly provided for. With a not always well-timed enthusiasm, the prodigal heaps pellet upon pellet, to the pitch of encumbering the burrow and making the mother's business difficult to carry on. Excessive wealth is an incubus. The thoughtless Beetle recognizes the fact at last and ejects the superfluous food from the shaft.

On the first day of June, in one of my appliances, the sum of pellets sent down amounts to 239, a number that speaks well for the trident-bearer's industry. My record of the droppings, kept as strictly as a banker's account, confirms the enormous result. I am overjoyed by the treasure of the Minotaurs'; but, a few days later, an unexpected issue alarms me. One morning I find the mother dead. She has come up to breathe her last on the surface. It appears to be the rule that neither of the pair shall die in the children's home. It is at a distance, in the open air, that the father and mother meet their end.

This reversal of the normal order of decease, the mother dying before the father, calls for enquiry. I inspect the inside of the apparatus by unscrewing the three movable shutters. My precautions against dryness have been fully successful. The uppermost third of the column of sand has retained a certain moisture which gives firmness and prevents any landslips. The middle third, with its sheath of wet rags, is even more moist. Here the victuals are heaped up in a well-stored granary; the male is there, brisk and energetic. In the lowest third, which stands in the wet earth of a large flower-pot, the plasticity is as great as that which my spade encounters in the deep natural burrow. Everything seems to be in order; and yet there is not a trace of nest-building at the bottom of the shaft; there are no sausages prepared or even preparing. All the pellets are untouched.

It is quite obvious: the mother has refused to lay and consequently the father has refrained from grinding. Directly the knead-ing of loaves is discontinued, meal becomes useless. The harvest is none the less plen-tiful, in view of future events. The 239 pel-lets to which my notes bear witness are there, in their original condition and divided into several heaps. The shaft is not straight; it has spiral slopes, it has landings communicating with little warehouses. Here are kept in reserve, at every level of the shaft, treasures which the mother will be able to employ even after the hoarder's decease. Pending the arrival of the eggs and the preparation of the loaves on the offsprings' behalf, the zealous father keeps on collecting, storing a little of the food at the bottom of his dwelling and a great deal more in lateral chambers, distributed over several floors.

But the eggs are wanting. What can the reason be? I begin by perceiving that the shaft runs down to the bottom of the apparatus, which is 55 inches high. It stops suddenly at the board which closes the bottom of the prism. This insuperable obstacle shows signs of attempted erosion. The mother, therefore, dug as long as digging was possible; then, coming to a barrier against which all her efforts failed, she climbed back to the surface, worn out and disheartened, having nothing left to do but die, for lack of an establishment to suit her.

Could she not lodge her eggs at the bottom of the prism, where a degree of moisture is maintained equal to that of the natural burrows? Perhaps not. In my part of the world, we had a very peculiar spring in this year 1906. It snowed hard on the 22nd and 23rd of March. Never in this district had I seen so heavy and especially so late a fall of snow. It was followed by an endless drought, which turned the country into a dust-heap.

In the apparatus, in which my watchful care maintained the requisite moisture, the mother Minotaur seemed protected against this calamity. There is nothing to tell us, however, that she was not fully cognizant, through the thickness of the planks, of what was happening, or rather about to happen, outside. Gifted with an exquisite sense of atmosphere, she had a presentiment of the terrible drought, fatal to grubs lodged too near the surface. Being unable to reach the deep places recommended by instinct, she died without laying her eggs. I see no other reason than this distrustful meteorology capable of accounting for the facts.

The second apparatus, two days after the installation of the couple, provides me with a grievous surprise. The mother, for no apparent cause, leaves the house, goes to earth in the sand on the tray and does not budge, heedless of the cell where her horned mate awaits her. Seven times over, at one day's interval, do I carry her home, dropping her head foremost down the shaft. It is of no avail: she climbs back persistently during the night, makes off and goes to earth as far away as possible. If the trellis work of the cover did not restrain her flight, she would run away for good, seeking another husband elsewhere. Can the first be dead? Not at all. I find him hale and hearty as ever in the upper level of the pit.

Can these stubborn attempts at escape on the part of the mother, so stay-at-home by nature, be caused by incompatibility of temper? Why not? The female worker goes away because the male worker does not please her. It was I myself who made the match, which was subject to the hazard of my discoveries; and the suitor has not found favour. If things had happened according to rule, the bride would have made a choice, accepting this one and refusing that, guided by merits of which she alone could judge. When a couple plan a long life together, they do not lightly enter into indissoluble bonds. This at least is the opinion of the Minotaur family.

That others, the vast majority, should

become friends, fall out and make it up again, in sudden and fortuitous encounters, is a matter of no consequence. Life is short; they enjoy it as best they may, without being too particular. But here we have the true household, enduring and laborious. How is it possible to toil in double harness for the welfare of the offspring without mutual sympathy? We have already seen the Minotaur couple recognizing each other and coming together again amid the confusion resulting from the upheaval of two adjoining burrows; here we find it subject to quite as sensitive a repugnance. The ill-mated bride sulks; she means to get away at all costs.

As the divorce seems destined to be indefinitely prolonged, despite the calls to order which I repeat day after day for a week by restoring the female to her burrow, I end by changing the male. I replace him by another, no better—and no worse-looking than was the first. Henceforth matters resume their normal course and all is as well as can be. The shaft is deepened, the outside mound is raised, the provisions are stored away, the factory of preserved foodstuffs is in full swing.

More Beetles

On the 2nd of June, the total number of pellets carried down amounts to 225. It is a splendid hoard. Shortly after, the father dies of old age. I find him near the mouth of the burrow, convulsively clutching his last pellet which he had not had time to carry down. The malady of age has surprised him in the midst of his labours, has struck him down on the harvest-field.

The widow continues her domestic work. To the riches amassed by the deceased, she adds, by her own activity, in the course of the month, thirty more pellets, making in all, since the foundation of the household, 255. Then comes the great heat, which favours idleness and slumber. The mother does not show herself any longer.

What does she do down below, in her cool cellar? Like the Copris mother apparently, she looks after her brood, going from cell to cell, sounding the cakes, investigating what is happening inside. It would be an act of barbarism to disturb her. We will wait till she comes out, accompanied by her offspring.

Let us profit by this long interval of rest to set forth the little that I have gathered from my attempts at rearing the Minotaur in a glass tube on the regulation diet. The egg takes about four weeks to hatch. The first that I find, dating from the 17th of April, gives birth to a grub on the 15th of May. This slow process of hatching can be due only to an insufficiency of heat in the early spring: underground, at a depth of five feet, the temperature hardly varies.

For that matter, we shall see the larva likewise taking its time and going through the whole summer before changing into the adult insect. It is so snug inside a sausage, in a cellar free from atmospheric variations, far from the hurly-burly of the outer world, where rejoicings are not unattended by danger; it is so sweet to do nothing, to indulge in digestive slumbers! Why hurry? The bustle of active life will come but too soon. The Minotaurs seem to hold that opinion: they prolong as far as may be the bliss of infancy.

The grub which has just been born in the sand pegs away with its legs and mandibles, strains and heaves with its rump, makes itself a passage and, from one day to the next, reaches the provisions piled up above it. In the glass tube in which I rear it I see it climbing, slipping into crevices, making a selection from the food about it and capriciously tasting on this side and on that. It coils and uncoils, it wriggles about, it sways to and fro. It is happy. So am I, to see it satisfied and glistening with health. I shall be able to watch its progress to the end.

In a couple of months' time, now ascending, now descending through its column of food and stopping at the best places, it is a handsome larva, well-shaped, neither fat nor spare, not unlike the Cetonia-grub in appearance. Its hind-legs have none of the shocking irregularity that used to surprise me so greatly when I was studying the family of the Geotrupes.

The grub of the last-named has hind-legs weaker than the rest, twisted, unfit for walking and turned over on its back. It is born a cripple. The grub of the Minotaur, despite the close analogy between the two dung-workers, is exempt from this infirmity. Its third pair of legs is no less accurate in shape and arrangement than the two other pairs. Why is the Geotrupes knock-kneed at birth and his close kinsman perfect? This is one of those little secrets of which it is only fitting that we should know how to admit our ignorance.

The larval stage ends in the last days of

Further Observations

August. Under the grub's digestive efforts, the food-column, while retaining its form and its dimensions, has been converted into a paste whose origin it would be impossible to recognize. There is not a crumb left in which the microscope can detect a fibre. The Sheep had already divided the vegetable matter very finely; the grub, an incomparable triturator, has taken the aforesaid matter and subdivided it yet further, grinding it after a fashion. In this way it extracts and uses the nutritive particles of which the Sheep's fourfold stomach is unable to take advantage.

To dig itself a cell in this unctuous mass ought, according to our logic, to suit the grub, desirous of a yielding mattress for the nymph to lie on. We are mistaken in our suppositions. The grub retreats to the lower end of its column, retires into the sand where the hatching took place and there makes itself a hard, rough cavity. This aberration, which takes no account of the future nymph, and its delicate skin, would be likely to surprise us if the homely dwelling were not subjected to improvement.

The hermit's wallet has retained a part of the digestive residues, residues destined to

147

disappear completely, for at the moment of
the nymphosis the body must be free of any
impurity. With this cement, which has undergone a prolonged refining in the intestine,
the grub plasters its sandy wall. Using its
round rump as a trowel, it smooths, polishes
and repolishes the layer of stucco, until the
rude cell of the start becomes a velvet-lined
chamber.

All is ready for the stripping that releases
the nymph. This nymph has peculiarities
deserving special mention. The male's trident, in particular, is already, both in shape
and size, what it will be in the adult Beetle.
At last, when October is at hand, I obtain the
perfect insect. The total period of development, beginning with the egg, has lasted five
months.

Let us return to the Minotaur mother who
is provided with 255 pellets, 225 of which
were amassed by the male, before he went
out to die, and 30 by the widow herself.
When the great heat comes, she no longer
shows herself at all, detained at the bottom
of the shaft by her domestic duties. In spite
of my impatience to know what is going on
indoors, I wait, keeping ever on the watch.
At last October brings the first rains, so

greatly wished for by the husbandman and the Dung-beetle alike. Recent mounds become numerous in the fields. This is the season of autumnal rejoicings, when the soil, which has been like a cinder all the summer, recovers its moisture and is covered with green grass to which the shepherd leads his flock; it is the festival of the Minotaur, the exodus of the youngsters who, for the first time, enter into the joys of the daylight, among the sugar-plums dropped by the Sheep in the pastures.

However, nothing appears under the cover of my apparatus. It is no use waiting any longer, the season is too far advanced. I take the pylon to pieces. The mother is dead; she is even in tatters, a sign of an end already remote. I find her at the top of the vertical shaft, not far from the orifice.

This position seems to show that, when her work was done, the mother climbed up to die out of doors as the father had done before her. A sudden and final break-down overcame her on the way, almost at her door. I expected something better; I pictured her coming out accompanied by her offspring: the plucky creature deserved to see her family revelling in the last fine days of the year.

More Beetles

I do not abandon this idea of mine. If the mother did not come out with the youngsters, there must have been—and in fact there were, as we shall see—important reasons for it. Right at the bottom of the column of sand, in the part which is coolest thanks to the large, frequently watered flower-pot, are eight sausages, eight portions of preserved food admirably worked into a fine paste. These are grouped in different stories, close together and each communicating with the main corridor by a short passage. Since each of these sausages was a ration, the brood amounts to eight. This restricted family was anticipated. When rearing becomes a costly matter, the mothers wisely limit their fecundity.

But here is an unexpected state of affairs: the food-cylinders contain no adult, not even a nymph; they have nothing but grubs in them, though these are glossy with health and almost fat enough to clamour for nymphosis. This check in their development arouses surprise, at a time when the new generation is full-grown, leaves the native homestead and is beginning to dig the winter burrows. The Minotaur mother's surprise must have exceeded my own. Weary of waiting for her offspring, she decided to set out by herself before her strength was completely exhausted, lest she should block the ascending shaft. A spasm, due to the inexorable toxin of old age, struck her down almost on the threshold of the dwelling.

The reason for this abnormal prolongation of the larval state escapes me. Perhaps it should be attributed to some hygienic flaw in my rearing-apparatus. It is obvious that all my care was unable to realize fully the conditions of well-being which the grubs would have found in the dampness of a deep, unlimited soil. Within a narrow prism of sand, too much exposed to the variations of temperature and humidity, feeding did not take place with the customary appetite and growth was slower in consequence. After all, these belated larvæ appear to be in first-rate fettle. I expect to see them undergo their transformation at the end of the winter. Like the young shoots whose development is interrupted by the inclemency of the season, they await the stimulus of spring.

CHAPTER VII

MINOTAURUS TYPHŒUS : MORALITY

THIS is the moment to recapitulate the
Minotaur's merits. When the severe
cold is over, he sets forth in quest of a mate,
buries himself with her and thenceforth remains faithful to her, despite his frequent
trips out of doors and the meetings to which
these are likely to lead. With indefatigable
zeal, he assists the burrower, herself destined
never to leave her home until the emancipa-
tion of the family. For a month and longer,
he loads the rubbish of the excavation on his
forked hod; he carries it up outside and remains ever patient, never disheartened by his
arduous feats of climbing. He leaves the
easy work of the excavating rake to the
mother and reserves for himself the more
troublesome task, the exhausting transport
through a narrow, perpendicular shaft of
great depth.

Next, the navvy becomes a collector of
foodstuffs; he goes catering and gathers the

wherewithal for his children to live upon.
To ease the work of his mate, who shreds
and compresses the preserved foodstuffs,
packing it away in layers, he once more
changes his trade and becomes a miller. At
some distance from the bottom, he bruises
and crumbles the materials found hardened
by the sun; he makes them into a meal and
flour which gradually pour down into the maternal bake-house. Lastly, worn out by his
efforts, he leaves the home and goes out to
die at a distance, in the open air. He has
gallantly performed his duty as the head
of a family; he has spent himself without
stint to secure the prosperity of his offspring.

The mother, on her side, allows nothing
to divert her from her housekeeping.
Throughout her working life, she never goes
out: *domi mansit,* as the ancients used to say
of their model matrons: she stays at home,
kneading her cylindrical loaves, filling them
with an egg, watching them until the exodus
arrives. When the time comes for the autumnal merry-making, she at last returns to
the surface, accompanied by her youngsters,
who disperse at will to feast in places frequented by the Sheep. Thereupon, having

nothing left to do, the devoted creature perishes.

Yes, amid the general indifference of the fathers towards their offspring, *Minotaurus* displays a most remarkable zeal where his family is concerned. Forgetful of himself, refusing to be led away by the rapturous delights of spring, at a time when it would be so pleasant to see a little of the country, to feast among his fellows, to tease and flirt with his fair neighbours, he sticks to his work underground and wears himself out to leave a fortune to his family. Here is one who, when his limbs stiffen in death, is well entitled to say:

"I have done my duty; I have worked."

Now whence did this industrious labourer derive his self-abnegation and his ardour for the welfare of his young? Men tell us that he acquired them by a slow progress from middling to good, from good to excellent. Fortuitous circumstances, hostile one day, favourable the next, have taught him what he knows. He has learnt, as man does, by experience: he too develops, progresses and improves himself.

In his little Dung-beetle brain, the lessons of the past leave lasting impressions which, matured by time, ripen into more considered actions. Necessity is the supreme inspirer of the instincts. Spurred by necessity, the animal is its own artisan; by its own energies it has made itself as we know it, with its implements and its trade. Its habits, its capacity and dexterity are integrals of infinite minuteness acquired on the illimitable path of time.

Such is the argument of the theorists, an argument sufficiently imposing to allure any independent mind, did not the empty resonance of words usurp the full sonority of reality. Let us question the Minotaur about all this. To be sure, he will not reveal to us the origin of instinct; he will leave the problem as obscure as ever; but he will at least be able to cast a glimmer into some little corner; and any light, however faint, even the flickering light of a taper, must be welcome in the dark tavern into which the animal leads us.

The Minotaur works exclusively with Sheep-droppings; for the purposes of his family, he needs them dry, toughened to the consistency of horn by long exposure to the sun. This choice seems very strange, when we remember that other stercoral collectors insist upon fresh products. The Sacred Beetle, the Copris, the Onthophagus:[1] not one of these, nor any of the others, cares for this sort of provender. All, whether large or small, whether modellers of pears or manufacturers of sausages, absolutely require plastic materials, retaining their full flavour.

The trident-bearer needs the pastoral olive, the Sheep's sugar-plum drained of all its juices. There is room in this world for tastes of every kind; the wisest thing is not to discuss them. Nevertheless, one would like to know why, when he is surrounded by such abundance of tender and succulent victuals, deriving from the Sheep or elsewhere, the three-pronged Dung-beetle selects what the others scornfully refuse. If he has not an innate predilection for this diet, how did he come to throw over the excellent, in which he had the right to share with the rest, and adopt the inferior, which is not employed elsewhere?

We will not labour the point. It amounts to this, that somehow the dry pellets have fallen to the Minotaur's share. This detail admitted, the rest unfolds itself with insis-

[1] Cf. *The Sacred Beetle and Others:* chaps. xi., xvii. and xviii.—*Translator's Note.*

tent logic. Necessity, the instigator of progress, seems to have gradually trained the
male Minotaur in his functions as a collaborator. The father of yore, an idler, as is
the rule among insects, has become an ardent
worker because, what with one experiment
after another, the race has benefited.

What does he do with his harvest? He
soberly feeds on it, when the moisture in the
burrow has somewhat softened the thankless
morsels; he cards great quantities of them
into a felt in which he buries himself in the
winter to shield himself against the cold.
But these are the lesser uses of his plunder;
the main thing is the future of the family.

Now the grub, whose stomach is at first
so squeamish, would never bite into such
snacks as these, if they were left untouched.
If they are to be accepted and relished, they
must be subjected to a refining which will
give them tenderness and flavour. In what
laboratory is the cooking to be done? Obviously underground, the only place where
an equable moisture prevails, free from the
unwholesome excess of humidity. Thus the
quality of the food gives rise to the
burrow.

And this burrow has to be deep, very deep,

in order that the scorching heat of summer may never reach them and render them useless by drying them up. The grub develops slowly; it will not attain the adult form until September. In its underground home, it has to brave with impunity the hottest and driest period of the year, without running the risk of finding its bread too stale. A depth of five feet is not too much to save the grub and its food from the fiery floods of sunlight in the dog-days.

The mother has the strength to dig a pit of this kind by herself, however deep it may be. No one will come to her assistance in her untiring work of excavation; but at the same time the rubbish has to be shot outside, so that the shaft may be always clear. This is needed first for the going and coming during the storage of victuals and later for the easy emergence of the offspring.

Boring and carrying would be too much for a single worker: the warm season would be too short for such a task. Thus, thereupon, long prepared by the events of each successive year, a flash of light penetrates the Dung-beetle's brain. The father says to himself:

Morality

"Let's lend a hand. It will make things go faster and better. I have three horns which I will use as a hod. I propose to offer my services to the digger and to hoist the loosened soil to the surface."

Working in double harness is invented; the household is founded. Other cares, no less urgent, confirm the agreement. The Minotaur's victuals, those compact morsels, have first to be broken up, bruised and reduced to particles which will lend themselves better to the elaboration of the final cake. After passing through the mill, the material must be carefully compressed into a cylinder, in which fermentation will complete the development of the requisite qualities. The whole business is a slow and meticulous work.

To shorten it, therefore, and to make the most of the fine weather, they set up in couples. The father collects the raw materials outside. On the upper floor, he turns his harvest into meal. On the lower floor, the mother receives the grist, sifts it and packs it into a column, gently patting down each layer. She kneads the dough for which her mate furnishes the flour. She works at the kneading-trough, he at the mill. Thus, by sharing the labour, they hasten the result and make the very utmost of the brief time at their disposal.

So far, all is well. Had they learnt their trade in the school of the centuries, through experiments of their own devising which proved successful from time to time, they would behave no differently. But now things begin to go awry. There is a reverse to the medal which proclaims the contrary of what we read on the obverse.

The cake that has just been prepared is the ration of one grub, absolutely of one alone. The prosperity of the race calls for more. Well, what happens? This, that the father leaves the house as soon as the first ration is prepared; the assistant deserts the baker and goes off to die at a distance. The excavations made in the meadows at the beginning of April always give me the two sexes: the father at the top of the house, engaged in shaping the pellets; the mother down at the bottom, working on the stacked provisions. A little later, the mother, is always alone: the father has disappeared.

As the laying is not over, the survivor has to continue the work unaided. True, the deep burrow, which cost so much time and trouble, is ready; so is the cell of the first-born of the family; but the others have to be provided for and it would be advantageous to rear as many of them as possible. The installation of each demands that the female, who until now has led a sedentary life, should often venture abroad. The stay-at-home becomes an out-of-doors collector; she gathers the pellets in the neighbourhood, brings them to the pit, stores them, breaks them up, kneads them and packs them into cylinders.

And it is at this moment of maternal activity that the father abandons the home! He excuses himself on the score of his decrepitude. He lacks not good-will but life itself. Reluctantly he retires, worn out with years.

We might reply:

"Considering that the successive stages of evolution have made you invent first housekeeping in common, a sublime discovery, and then the deep cellar, tending to keep the preserves in good condition during the summer; the grinding-process which gives plasticity and prevents dryness; and the packing into sausages, in which the materials ferment and improve: considering all this, could not that same evolution teach you to prolong your life for a few weeks? With the aid of a most carefully conducted selection, the affair does not strike me as impracticable. In one of my appliances, the male held out until June, after placing a treasure-house of pellets at his mate's disposal."

He in like manner would be entitled to say:

"The Sheep is not always very generous. The crops are lean around the burrow; and, when I have rolled the few available victuals into the burrow, I soon pine away, worn out by unemployment. If my colleague survived till June in a scientific apparatus, it was because he was surrounded by inexhaustible riches. The power of storing as much as he pleased made life sweet to him; the certainty of work lengthened his days. I am not as well-provided for as he and I allow myself to die of boredom when I have finished gathering the poor harvest in my neighbourhood."

"Very well; but you have wings, you are able to fly. Why do you not go some distance away? You would find enough to satisfy your passion for hoarding. But you don't do this. Why? Because time has not taught you the fruitful device of making excursions a few steps from your home. How is it that, in order to assist your mate till the end of her labours, you have not yet learnt to keep up your courage for a few days longer and glean a little farther all around your home? . . . If evolution which, as they say, has instructed you in your difficult trade, has nevertheless allowed you to remain in ignorance of these highly important details, which are easy to carry out after a short apprenticeship, the reason is because it has taught you nothing at all, whether housekeeping, burrowing or baking. Your evolution is a permanent affair. You move about within a circle with a fixed radius; you are and always will be what you were when the first pellet was lowered into the cellar."

All this explains nothing. True; but to know how not to know at least gives a stable equilibrium and repose to our restless curiosity. We are very near the precipice of the unknowable. That precipice should be engraved with what Dante inscribes on the gate of his Inferno:

"*Lasciate ogni speranza.*"

Yes, let all of us who, when we take the atom by assault, imagine that we are storming the universe: let us abandon all hope here. The sanctuary of origin will not be opened for us. In vain do we seek to fathom the riddle of life: we shall never attain the exact truth. The hook of theory catches nothing but illusions, acclaimed to-day as the last word of knowledge, rejected as false to-morrow and replaced by others which are sooner or later seen to be erroneous in their turn. Where then is this truth? Does it, like the asymptote of the geometricians, recede into infinity, pursued by our curiosity, which always draws nearer to it without ever reaching it?

This comparison would be suitable were our knowledge a curve of uniform development; but it goes forwards and backwards, up and down, twists and turns, approaches its asymptote and then suddenly runs away from it. It may chance to cross it, but only unconsciously. The full knowledge of the truth escapes it.

Be this as it may, the Minotaur couple, in so far as our casual observations enable us to see, are remarkably zealous where the family is concerned. We should have to go high indeed in the animal series to find similar instances. Furred and feathered life will afford us hardly any equivalents.

If such things occurred, not in the Dung-beetle world but in our own, we should speak of them as pertaining to a very fine morality.

Morality

The expression would be out of place here. Animals have no morality. It is known to man alone, who formulates it and improves upon it gradually in the light of his conscience, that sensitive mirror in which is concentrated all that is best within us.

The advance of this improvement, the loftiest of all, is extremely slow. Cain, the first murderer, after slaying his brother, reflected a little, we are told. Was this remorse on his part? Apparently not, but rather apprehension of a hand stronger than his own. The fear of punishment to reward the crime was the beginning of wisdom.

And this fear was justified, for Cain's successors were singularly skilled in the art of constructing homicidal engines. After the fist came the stick, the club, the stone thrown by the sling. Progress brought the flint arrow-head and ax and later the bronze sword, the iron pike, the steel blade. Chemistry took a hand in the business and must be awarded the palm for extermination. In our own day, the wolves of Manchuria could tell us what orgies of human flesh they owe to improved explosives.

What has the future in store for us? One dares not think of it. Piling at the roots of

More Beetles

our mountains, picrate on dynamite, pan-
clactite on fulminate and other explosives a
thousand times more powerful, which science, ever in progress, will not fail to invent,
shall we end by blowing up the planet?
Thrown into confusion by the shock, will the
ragged splinters of the terrestrial clod whirl
away in vortices like that of the asteroids,
the apparent ruins of a vanished world?
This would be the end of all great and noble
things, but it would be the end also of much
that is ugly and much that is pitiful.

In our day, with materialism in full sway,
we have physics working precisely at demol-
ishing matter. It pulverizes the atom, sub-
tilizing it until it disappears, transformed
into energy. The tangible and visible mass
is only appearance; in reality all is force. If
the knowledge of the future succeeded in
harking back on a large scale to the primordial origins of matter, a few slabs of rock,
suddenly disintegrated into energy, would
dislocate the glove into a chaos of forces.
Then Gilbert's [1] great word-picture would
be realized:

[1] Nicolas Joseph Laurent Gilbert (1751-1780), a
satirical poet, many strophes of whose *Adieux à la Vie*
have become classic.—*Translator's Note.*

Morality

*"Et d'ailes et de faux dépouillé désormais,
Sur les mondes detruits le temps dort,
    immobile."* [1]

But do not rely overmuch on these heroic
remedies. Let us take Candide's [2] advice
and cultivate our garden; let us water our
cabbage-patch and accept things as they are.

Nature, a ruthless wet-nurse, knows nothing of pity. After pampering her charges,
she takes them by the foot, whirls them
round her head and dashes them to pieces
against a rock. This is her way of diminishing the burden of her excessive fertility.

Death, well and good; but of what use is
pain? When a mad Dog endangers the
public safety, do we speak of inflicting atrocious sufferings upon him? We put a bullet
into him; we do not torture him: we defend
our own lives. In the old days, however, the
law, with a great parade of ermine and red
gowns, used to draw and quarter criminals,
to break them on the wheel, to roast them
at the stake, to burn them in a brimstone
shirt: it pretended to expiate the crime by
the horror of the torture. Morality has

[1] "And thenceforth, of his wings and scythe despoiled,
    Time sleeps, unmoving on the worlds destroyed."
[2] Voltaire's story of that name.—*Translator's Note.*

167

made great strides since then; in our time, a more enlightened conscience compels us to treat the wrong-doer with the same clemency that we show to the mad Dog. We put an end to his existence without any stupid refinements of cruelty.

It even seems as though a day would come when legal murder will disappear from our codes: instead of killing the criminal, we shall strive to cure his infirmity. We shall fight the virus of crime as we fight that of yellow fever or of the plague. But when may we expect to see this absolute respect for human life? Will it take hundreds and thousands of years to come into being? Possibly. Conscience is so slow in emerging from its slough.

Ever since there have been men on this earth, morality has been far from saying its last word even on the subject of the family, that pre-eminently hallowed group. The ancient *paterfamilias* is a despot in his own house. He rules over his household as over the herd in his demesne; he has rights of life and death over his children, disposes of them at will, barters them in exchange for others, sells them into slavery, brings them up for his own sake and not for theirs.

Morality

Primitive legislation displays a revolting brutality in this respect.

Things have improved considerably since
then, though the ancient barbarism has not
been wholly abolished. Is there any lack of
people among ourselves to whom morality
is reduced to a fear of the police? Could we
not find many who rear their children, as we
breed Rabbits, to make a profit out of them?
It has been necessary to formulate the
promptings of conscience into a strict law in
order to save the child, up to the age of thirteen, from the hell of the factories where the
poor little fellow's future was destroyed for
a few halfpence a day.

Though animals have no morality, which
is a thing troublesome to acquire and always
undergoing improvement in the brains of the
philosophers, they have their commandments, laid down in the beginning, immu-
table, imperious and as deeply imprinted in
their being as the need to breathe and eat.
At the head of the commandments stands
maternal solicitude. Since life's primary object is the continuation of life, it is also essential that the fragile beginnings of existence
should be made possible. It is the mother's
duty to see to this.

More Beetles

No mother neglects this duty. The dullest at least lay their germs in propitious places, where the new-born offspring will of themselves find the wherewithal to live. The best-endowed suckle, spoon-feed or store food for their children, build nests, cells or nurseries, often masterpieces of exquisite delicacy. But as a rule, especially in the insect class, the fathers become indifferent to their progeny. We, who have not yet laid aside all our old savagery, do the same to a small extent.

The decalogue orders us to honour our father and mother. This would be perfect, if it were not silent as to the duties of the father towards his sons. It speaks as once the tyrant of the family clan used to speak, the *paterfamilias*, referring everything to himself and caring but little for others. It took a long time to make people understand that the present owes itself to the future and that the father's first duty is to prepare the sons for the harsh struggles of life.

Others, among the humblest, have outstripped it. Prompted by an unconscious inspiration, they straightway resolved the paternal problem, which among us is still obscure. The Minotaur father in particular, if he had a vote in these grave matters, would amend our decalogue. He would move to add, in simple lines imitated from our catechism:

"Bring up your children in the way they should do."

CHAPTER VIII

THE ERGATES ; THE COSSUS

THIS is Shrove Tuesday, a relic of the saturnalia of old; and I have it in my mind to do some strange cooking, which would have delighted the soul of a Roman gourmet. When I let my imagination run away with me, I want my folly to achieve some measure of notoriety. I must have witnesses, connoisseurs who will be able, each in his fashion, to appreciate the merits of an unknown fare of which none but the classical scholar has ever heard before. A question so serious must be debated in council.

There will be eight of us: my family, to begin with, and then two friends, probably the only persons in the village in whose presence I may venture on these eccentricities of the table without provoking comments on what would be regarded as a depraved taste.

One of them is the schoolmaster. Let us call him by his name, Julian, as he has no objection and is not afraid of what foolish people will say if ever they get to hear of our banquet. He is a man of liberal views and scientific training, whose mind is always open to admit the truth in any guise.

The second, Marius Guigne, is blind. A joiner by trade, he wields his saw and plane in the blackest darkness with as sure a hand as any skilled craftsman who enjoys the full use of his eyes can exercise in broad daylight. He lost his sight when a boy, after knowing the blessings of the sunshine and the miracles of colour. To make up for the perpetual gloom in which he lives, he has acquired a gentle and ever-cheerful philosophy, a passionate desire to fill as best he can the gaps left by his meagre primary education, an ear exquisitely refined in musical matters and a sensitiveness of skin which is very unusual in fingers hardened by the labour of the carpenter's shop. When he and I are talking, if he wants to know something about this or that geometrical property, he holds out his hand to me, wide open. It is our black-board. I trace with my forefinger the figure to be constructed and accompany the light contact with a short explanation. That is enough to make him understand the idea which the plane, the saw and the lathe will translate into actuality.

On Sunday afternoons, especially in winter, when three or four logs blazing on the hearth afford a pleasant change from the fierce blast of the mistral, these two meet at my house. We three form the village Athenæum, the rustic Academy where everything is discussed except the hateful subject, politics. Philosophy, morals, literature, philology, science, history, numismatics, archæology by turns furnish matter for our exchange of ideas, in accordance with the unforeseen twists of the conversation. At one of these gatherings, which lighten my solitude, today's dinner was plotted. The unusual dish consists of Cossi, a famous delicacy in the days of antiquity.

The Romans, when they had devoured their fill of nations, besotted by excessive luxury, took to eating worms. Pliny tells us:

"Romanis in hoc luxuria esse coepit, praegrandesque roborum vermes delicatiore sunt in cibo; cossus vocant." [1]

What are these worms exactly? The Latin naturalist is not very explicit; he tells

[1] "Luxury had reached such a pitch among the Romans that they looked upon the huge worms of the oak as a delicacy; they called them Cossi."

us nothing at all except that they live in the trunks of oaks. No matter: with this detail we cannot go astray. The worm in question is the larva of the Great Capricorn (*Cerambyx heros*).[1] A frequent inmate of the oak, it is, in fact, a lusty grub and attracts one's attention by its resemblance to a fat, white sausage. But the expression *prægrandesque roborum vermes* should, to my thinking, be generalized a little. Pliny was no precisian. Having occasion to speak of a big worm, he mentions that of the oak, the commonest of the larger ones; and he overlooks the others or takes them for granted, probably failing to distinguish them from the first.

Let us not keep too strictly to the tree mentioned in the Latin text, but consider what the old author had really in mind when he spoke of these worms. We shall find other worms no less worthy of the title of Cossus than the Oak-worm, for instance the worm of the chestnut-tree, the larva of the Stag-beetle.

One indispensable condition must be fulfilled to earn the celebrated name: the grub

[1] Cf. *The Glow-worm and Other Beetles:* chap. vii.—*Translator's Note.*

must be plump, of a good size and not too repulsive in appearance. Now by a curious
freak of scientific nomenclature it happens
that the name of Cossus has been allotted to
the mighty caterpillar [1] whose galleries
honeycomb old willows: a hideous, malodor-
ous creature, the colour of wine-lees. No
gullet, not even a Roman's, would have
dared to swallow anything so loathsome.
The Cossus of the modern naturalists is certainly not that of the epicures of old.

In addition to the larvæ of the Capricorn
and the Stag-beetle, which have been identi-
fied by the writers with Pliny's famous worm,
I know another which, in my opinion, would
fulfil the requisite conditions even better. I
will tell you how I discovered it.

The short-sighted law of the land has
nothing to say to the slayer of noble trees,
the unimaginative fool who, for a handful of
crown-pieces, pillages the stately woods, lays
bare the countryside, dries up the clouds and
turns the soil into a parching slag-heap.
There was in my neighbourhood a magnificent clump of pine-trees, the joy of the Black-
bird, the Thrush, the Jay, and other passers-
by, of whom I was one and not the least as-

[1] *Cossus ligniperda,* the caterpillar of *Xylentes cossus,*
the Great Goat-moth.—*Translator's Note.*

siduous. The owner had it cut down. Two
or three years after the massacre, I visited
the spot.

The pines had disappeared, converted into
timber and firewood; nothing remained but
the enormous stumps, which were too difficult to extract. They were doomed to rot
where they stood. Not only had the
weather left its marks upon them, but their
interior was full of wide galleries, the signs
of a vigorous population completing the
work of death begun by man. It struck me
that it would be as well to enquire what was
swarming inside them. The landlord had
made the most of his coppice; he left it to me
to make the most of the ideas which it suggested, since these had no value for him.

One fine afternoon in winter, all my family
foregather and, with my son Paul wielding
a heavy implement, we proceed to break up
a couple of stumps. The wood, hard and
dry outside, has been transformed inside into
very soft layers, like slabs of touchwood.
In the midst of this moist, warm decay, a
worm as thick as my thumb abounds. Never
have I seen a fatter one.

Its ivory whiteness is pleasing to the eye
and its satin-like delicacy is soft to the touch.

177

More Beetles

If we can for once emancipate ourselves from gastronomic prejudices, it is even appetizing, resembling as it does a translucent bag filled to bursting-point with fresh butter. At the sight of it, an idea occurs to us: this must be the Cossus, the true Cossus, far superior to the coarse grub of the Capricorn. Why not try the much-vaunted fare? Here is a capital opportunity, which perhaps will never occur again.

We gather a plentiful crop, therefore, in the first place so that we may study the grub, whose shape proclaims it to be the larva of a Longicorn, or Long-horned Beetle, and in the second place to investigate the culinary problem. We want to know what insect exactly is represented by this larva; we also want to discover the edible value of the Cossus. It is Shrove Tuesday, a propitious date for such extravagances of the table.

I know not with what sauce the Cossus was eaten in the days of the Cæsars; no Aepicus [1] of the period has bequeathed us any information in this respect. Ortolans are roasted skewered on a spit; to add the seasoning of

[1] Marcus Gabius Apicus, a famous Roman epicure who lived in the days of Augustus and Tiberius.—*Translator's Note.*

any complicated dressing would be a profana-
tion. Let us do the same with the Cossi,
those Ortolans of entomology. Stuck in a
row on a skewer, they are grilled over red-
hot charcoal. A pinch of salt, the necessary
condiment of our meats, is the only extraneous relish. The roast turns a golden
brown, shrivels slowly and sheds a few oily
tears, which take fire on touching the coal
and burn with a fine white flame. The dish
is ready. Let us serve it hot.

Encouraged by my example, my family bravely attack their skewerfuls. The
schoolmaster hesitates, a victim to his fancy,
which pictures the fat worms of a moment
ago crawling about his plate. He picks out
the smallest ones, as less likely to provoke
unpleasant reminiscences. The blind man is
not so much at the mercy of his imagination,
gives his undivided attention to the dish before him and eats with every sign of satisfaction.

All are of one opinion. The joint is juicy,
tender, and very savoury. The taste reminds one a little of burnt almonds flavoured
with the merest suggestion of vanilla. In
short, the dish of worms is pronounced to be
most agreeable, one might even say first-rate.

What would it not be if the art of the ancient epicures had been lavished on its cooking!

The skin alone leaves something to be desired: it is very tough. One might describe the new dish as the daintiest of force-meat, wrapped in parchment; the inside is delicious, but the outside defies the teeth. I offer it to my Cat: she refuses it, though she is very fond of sausage-skin. The two Dogs, my assiduous acolytes at dinner-time, refuse it likewise, refuse it obstinately, certainly not because of its hard texture, for their omnivorous gullets are sublimely indifferent to difficulties of deglutition. But their subtle sense of smell recognizes in the proffered morsel something unfamiliar, something absolutely unknown to all their race; and, after sniffing at it, they draw back as suspiciously as though I had offered them a mustard-sandwich. It is too new to them.

They remind me of the innocent wonder of my neighbours, the women of the village, when they pass in front of the fishwives' stalls at Orange on market-days. Here are baskets filled with Shell-fish, others with Crawfish, others with Sea-urchins.

"Eh," they ask one another, "are those things meant to be eaten? And how?

Roast or boiled? You wouldn't catch me tackling that stuff."

And, vastly surprised that there should be people capable of making a meal off anything so loathly, they turn aside from the Sea-urchin. Even so do my Cat and my Dogs. With them as with ourselves, exceptional food needs an apprenticeship.

To the little that he has to say about the Cossus, Pliny adds: *"Etiam farina saginati, hi quoque altiles sunt,"* which means that the worms were fattened with meal to improve their flavour. The recipe startled me at first, all the more so as the old naturalist is much given to this system of fattening. He tells us of one Fulvius Hirpinus who invented the art of rearing Snails, so highly esteemed by the gormandizers of the day. The herd destined to be fattened were placed in a park surrounded by water to prevent escape and furnished with earthenware vases to serve as shelters. Fed on a paste of flour and syrupy wine, the Snails became enormous. Notwithstanding all my respect for the venerable naturalist, I cannot believe that molluscs thrive so remarkably when put on a diet of flour and syrupy wine. These are childish exaggerations, which were inevitable at first, when the scientific spirit of research had not yet come into being. Pliny artlessly repeats the talk of the country folk of his day.

I have much the same doubts about the Cossi that put on flesh when fed with meal. Still, the result is less incredible than that alleged to take place in the Snail-park. As a scrupulous observer, let me test the method. I put a few grubs taken from the pines in a glass jar full of flour. They receive no other food. I expected to see the larvæ, smothered in that fine dust, dying quickly, either suffocated by the obstruction of their air-holes or perishing for lack of suitable nourishment.

Great was my mistake. Pliny was right: the Cossi thrive in the flour and feed heartily on it. I have before me some that have spent a year in this environment. They eat their way through it, scooping out corridors and leaving behind them a brown paste, the waste product of their digestive organs. That they are actually fatter I cannot state for a fact; but at least they have a magnificent appearance, no less imposing than that of others which were kept in jars filled with scraps of their native tree-stumps. The flour is amply sufficient, if not to fatten them, at least to keep them in excellent condition.

Enough of the Cossus and my crazy skewers. If I have studied the question so closely, it certainly has not been with the hope of enriching our bills of fare. No, that was not my object, even though Brillat-Savarin[1] has said that "the invention of a new dish is a greater benefit to humanity than the discovery of an asteroid." The scarcity of the pine-tree's plump inhabitants and the repugnance with which the vast majority of us view any sort of vermin will always prevent my new comestible from becoming a common article of diet. It is probable even that it will remain a mere curiosity, which people will take on trust without verifying its qualities. Not everybody has the needful independence of stomach to appreciate the merits of a worm.

Still less, so far as I was concerned, was the bait of a dainty dish the motive. My sober tastes are not easily tempted. A handful of cherries is more to my liking than all the preparations of our cookery-books. My sole desire was to throw light upon a point of

[1] Anthelme Brillat-Savarin (1755-1826), the famous French gastronomer, author of *La Physiologie du goût.*— *Translator's Note.*

183

natural history. Have I succeeded? It may well be that I have.

Let us now consider the metamorphoses of the grub; let us strive to obtain the adult form, so as to determine the nature of our subject, which has hitherto remained nameless. The rearing presents no difficulty whatever. I install my plump larvæ, straight from the pine-tree, in flower-pots of ordinary size. I provide them with a goodly heap of scraps from their old home, the tree-stump, choosing by preference the central layers, which have rotted into soft flakes of touchwood.

The grubs creep in and out of the well-stocked refectory at their own sweet will; they crawl lazily up and down or stand still, gnawing all the time. I need pay no further attention to them, provided the victuals remain fresh. With this rough and ready treat I have kept them in first-rate condition for a couple of years. My boarders have all the happy tranquillity that comes from an untroubled digestion; and they know nothing of home-sickness.

In the first week of July, I catch sight of a grub wiggling vigorously, turning round and round. This exercise is to give suppleness in

view of the coming moult. The violent
gymnastics take place in a large apartment of
no special structure, without cement or glaze.
The big grub, by rolling its rump to and fro,
has simply pushed back all around it the
powdery ligneous matter produced by its
crumbled or even digested provisions. It
has compressed and felted it together; and,
as I have taken care to keep the material
suitably moist, it sets into a fairly solid and
remarkably smooth wall. It is a stucco
made of wood-pulp.

A few days later, in stiflingly hot weather,
the grub sheds its skin. The moult is effected at night and I am therefore unable to
witness it; but next morning I have the
newly-divested clothing at my disposal. The
skin has been split open on the thorax up to
the first segment, which has released itself,
bringing the head with it. Through this narrow dorsal fissure, the nymph has issued by
alternately stretching and contracting, so
that the cast skin forms a crumpled bag,
which is almost intact.

On the day of its deliverance, the nymph
is a magnificent white, whiter than alabaster,
whiter than ivory. Add a slight transpar-
ency to the substance of our superfine stearin

candles and you will have something nearly resembling that budding flesh in process of crystallization.

The arrangement of the limbs is faultlessly symmetrical. The folded legs make one think of arms crossed upon the breast in a sacerdotal attitude. Our painters have no better symbol for representing mystic resignation to the hand of destiny. Joined together, the tarsi form two long, knotted cords that lie along the nymph's sides like a priest's stole. The wings and wing-cases, fitting by pairs into a common sheath, are flattened into wide paddles like flakes of talc. In front, the antennæ are bent into elegant crosiers and then slip under the knees of the first pair of legs and rest their tips on the wing-paddles. The sides of the corselet project slightly, like a head-dress recalling the spreading white caps of our French nuns.

My children, when I show them this wonderful creature, find a very happy phrase to describe it:

"It's a little girl making her first communion," they say, "a little girl in her white veil."

What a lovely gem, if it were permanent and incorruptible! An artist seeking for a decorative subject would find an exquisite model here. And this gem moves. At the least disturbance, it fidgets about on its back, very much like a Gudgeon laid high and dry on the river-bank. Feeling itself in danger, the terrified creature strives to make itself terrifying.

Next day, the nymph is clouded with a faint smoky tint. The work of a final transformation begins and is continued for a fortnight. At last, towards the end of July, the nymphal garment is reduced to shreds, torn by the movements of the stretching and waving limbs. The full-grown insect appears, clad in rusty-red and white. The colour soon becomes darker and gradually changes to black. The insect has completed its development.

I recognize it as the naturalists' *Ergates faber*, which, translated into the vernacular, means "the journeyman blacksmith." If any one knows why this long-horned Beetle, this lover of old pine-stumps, is called a working blacksmith, I will thank him to tell me.

The Ergates is a magnificent insect, vying with the Great Capricorn in size, but with broader wing-cases and a slightly flatter body.

More Beetles

The male carries on his corselet two broad, triangular, glistening facets. These constitute his blazon and serve no other purpose than that of masculine adornment.

I have tried to observe by lantern-light—for the insect is nocturnal in its habits—the nuptial charms of the blazoned Beetle of the pines in his native surroundings. My son Paul went all over the ravaged plantation, lantern in hand, between ten and eleven at night; he explored the old stumps one by one. The expedition led to nothing; no Ergates was seen, of either sex. We need not regret this failure: by rearing the insects in the cages we learn the most interesting details of the business.

I take the Beetles born in my study and install them, in isolated couples, under spacious wire-gauze dish-covers placed over stacks of refuse from the decayed pine-stumps. By way of food, I serve them with pears cut into quarters, small bunches of grapes and slices of melon, all favourite dainties of the Great Capricorn.

The captives rarely show themselves by day; they remain concealed under the heap of chips. They come out at night and solemnly stroll to and fro, now on the wire trellis, now on the pile of wood that represents the pine-stump to which they must hasten when the egg-laying season arrives. Never do they touch the provisions, though these are kept fresh by almost daily renewals; never do they nibble at the fruit, at the dainties in which the Capricorn delights. They scorn to eat.

Worse still: apparently they disdain to pair. I watch them every evening for nearly a month. What melancholy lovers! There is no eagerness on the part of the male, no impetuous hurry to woo his mate; no teasing on the part of the female to stimulate her backward swain. Each shuns the other's company; and, when they do meet, they merely maim each other. Under all my wire covers, five in number, sooner or later I find either the male or the female, sometimes both, the poorer by a few legs or one or both antennæ. The cut is so clean that it might be the work of a pruning-shears. The sharp edge of the mandibles, which are shaped like cleavers, explains this hacking. I myself, if I get my fingers caught, am bitten till the blood comes.

What kind of creatures are these, among whom the sexes cannot meet without mutilating each other, these savages with their ferocious embraces, whose caresses are sheer mangling! For blows to be exchanged between males, in the fierce brawl for the possession of the bride, is an everyday occurrence: it is the rule among the greater part of the animal creation. But here the female herself is sorely ill-treated, perhaps after having been the first to begin.

"Ah, you've damaged my plume!" says the journeyman blacksmith. "All right, I'll break your leg for you. Take that!"

More reprisals follow. The shears are brought into action on either side, and the fight produces a pair of cripples.

If the housing were inadequate, one could put down this brutality to the terrified hustling of a mob of maddened creatures; but one can no longer do so when a roomy cage leaves the two captives ample space for their nocturnal rambles. They lack nothing in the wire dome but liberty of flight. Could this deprivation tend to embitter their character? How far removed are they from the Common Capricorn! He, though he form one of a dozen huddled under the same dish-cover, for a month on end, without any neighbours' quarrel, bestrides his companion, and, from

time to time, caresses her with a lick of his
tongue on her back. Other people, other
customs. I know one who rivals the insect
of the pines in that barbarous propensity for
mutilating its fellows. This is the Ægosoma (*Æ. scabricorne,* FAB.*),* who likewise
is a lover of darkness and sports a pair of
long horns. His grub lives in the wood of
old willows hollow with age. The adult is
a handsome insect, attired in bright brown
and bearing a pair of very fierce antennæ.
With the Capricorn and Ergates, he is the
most noteworthy of all the Longicorns in the
matter of size.

In July, at about eleven o'clock on a warm,
still night, I find him crouching flat on the
inside of the cavernous willows or oftener on
the outside, on the rough bark of the trunk.
The males occur pretty frequently. Motionless, undismayed by the sudden flashes of my
lantern, they await the coming of the females
lurking in the deep crevices of the decayed
wood.

The Ægosoma also is armed with powerful shears, with mandibular cleavers which
are very useful to the new-formed adult for
hewing a way out, but which become a crying
abuse among insects of the same family,

when addicted to chopping off each other's legs and antennæ. If I do not isolate my subjects one by one in strong paper bags, I am certain, on returning from my nocturnal expeditions, to find none but cripples in my box. The mandibular knife has done furious execution on the way. Almost all the insects are the poorer by at least a leg.

In the wire cage, with chips of old willowwood for a refuge and figs, pears and other fruits for food, they are less intolerant. For three or four days, my captives betray great excitement at nightfall. They run swiftly along the trellised dome, quarrelling as they go, biting one another, striking at one another with their cleavers. In the absence of females, almost undiscoverable at the time of my visits, which are possibly not late enough, I have not been able to observe their nuptials; but I have seen acts of brutality that tell me something of what I want to know. No less expert in chopping off legs than his kinsman of the pines, the Ægosoma should also be somewhat deficient in gallantry. I picture him beating his wife and crippling her a little, not without himself receiving his share of wounds.

If these were Longicorn affairs, the scandal would not be far-reaching; but, alas, we also have our domestic quarrels! The Beetle explains his by his nocturnal habits: the light makes for milder manners; the darkness tends to deprave them. The result is worse when the soul is in darkness; and the lout who thrashes his wife is a child of the gloom.

CHAPTER IX

THE PINE COCKCHAFER

IN writing Pine Cockchafer at the head of
this chapter, I am guilty of a deliberate
heresy: the insect's orthodox name is Fuller
Cockchafer (*Melolontha fullo*, LIN.). We
must not be fastidious, I know, in matters of
nomenclature. Make a noise of some sort,
give it a Latin termination and you will have,
as far as euphony goes, the equivalent of
many of the labels pasted in the entomolo-
gist's specimen-boxes. The cacophony would
be excusable if the barbarous expression signi-
fied nothing else than the creature intended;
but, generally speaking, this name possesses,
hidden among its Greek or other roots, a certain meaning in which the novice hopes to
find a little information.

He will be woefully disappointed. The
scientific term refers to subtleties difficult to
grasp and of very slight importance. Too
often it leads him astray, suggesting views
which have naught in common with the truth

194

as we know it from observation. Sometimes
the errors are flagrant; sometimes the al-
lusions are grotesque and imbecile. Provided that they have a decent sound, how
greatly preferable are locutions in which entomology finds nothing to dissect!

Fullo would be one of these, if the word
had not a first sense which at once occurs to
the mind. This Latin expression means a
"fuller," one who "fulls" cloth under running water, dressing it and ridding it of the
stiffness of the weaving. What connection
has the Cockchafer who forms the subject of
this chapter with the working fuller? You
may rack your brains in vain: no acceptable
answer will come.

The term *fullo,* applied to an insect, occurs in Pliny. In one chapter the great
naturalist treats of remedies for jaundice,
fevers and dropsy. A little of everything
plays its part in this pharmacopœia: a black
Dog's longest tooth; a Mouse's nose
wrapped in a pink rag; a green Lizard's right
eye torn from the living reptile and placed
in a kid-skin bag; a Snake's heart, torn out
with the left hand; the four joints of a Scorpion's tail, including the sting, wrapped up
in a black cloth, provided that for three days

the patient can see neither the remedy nor
him that applied it; and many other extravagances. We close the book, alarmed by
the slough of absurdities whence the art of
healing has come down to us.

In this medley of inanities, the forerunner
of medicine, the fuller makes his appearance.
The text says:

*"Tertium qui vocatur fullo, albis guttis,
dissectum utrique lacerto adalligant."*

To treat fevers, we must divide the Fuller Beetle into two parts and fasten one half
to the right arm and the other half to the
left.

Now what did the ancient naturalist mean
by this term Fuller Beetle? We do not
know exactly. The description *albis guttis,*
white spots, would fit the white-flecked Pine-
chafer pretty well, but it is not enough to
make us certain. Pliny himself seems to
have been none too sure of his wonderful
cure. In his time, men's eyes had not yet
learnt how to look at the insect. The creatures were too small; they were fit amusement for children, who would tie them to
the end of a long thread and make them run

round in a circle, but they were unworthy the attention of a self-respecting man.

Pliny apparently got the word from the country-folk, always poor observers and inclined to bestow extravagant names. The scholar accepted the rustic locution, the work perhaps of a childish imagination, and applied it as a makeshift, without further enquiries. The word has come down to us a fragment of antiquity; our modern naturalists have adopted it; and this is how one of our handsomest insects became the Fuller. The majesty of the centuries has consecrated the strange appellation.

In spite of all my respect for ancient languages, the term Fuller does not appeal to me because in the circumstances it is nonsensical. Common sense should take precedence of the aberrations of nomenclature. Why not say Pine Cockchafer, in memory of the beloved tree, the paradise of the insect during the two or three weeks of its aërial life? It would be very simple; nothing could be more natural: a very good reason for putting it last of all.

We have to wander a long time in the night of absurdity before reaching the radiant light of truth. All our sciences bear witness to this, even the science of number. Try to add a column of figures written in Roman numerals: you will abandon the task, stupefied by the confusion of the symbols, and you will realize how great a revolution was made in arithmetic by the invention of the figure nought. Like the egg of Columbus, it was indeed a very small thing, but it had to be thought of.

Until the future casts the unfortunate Fuller into oblivion, we will say Pine Cockchafer, so far as we are concerned. Using this name, no one can make a mistake: our insect frequents the pine-tree only. It has a handsome and portly appearance, vying with that of *Oryctes nasicornis*.[1] Its costume, though not boasting the metallic splendour dear to the Carabus,[2] the Buprestis,[3] and the Cetonia, is at least unusually elegant. A black or brown ground is thickly strewn with capricious spots of white velvet. It is at the same time modest and magnificent.

By way of plumes, the male wears at the

[1] The Rhinoceros Beetle. Cf. *The Glow-worm and Other Beetles:* chap. xiii.—*Translator's Note.*

[2] Cf. Chapters xiii. and xiv. of the present volume.—*Translator's Note.*

[3] Cf. *The Glow-worm and Other Beetles:* chaps. viii. and xiv.—*Translator's Note.*

end of his short antennæ seven large super-posed leaves, which, opening and closing like a fan, betray the emotions of the moment. At first sight one would take this superb foliage for a sense-organ of great perfection, capable of perceiving subtle odours, almost inaudible waves of sound or other means of information unknown to our senses; but the female warns us not to go too far in this direction. Her maternal duties demand that she should possess a susceptibility to impressions at least as great as that of the other sex; and yet her antennary plumes are very small and consist of six niggardly leaves.

Then what is the use of the male's enor-mous fan? The seven-leaved apparatus is to the Pine-chafer what his long, quivering horns are to the Capricorn and the panoply of the forehead to the Onthophagus and the forked antlers of the mandibles to the Stag-beetle. Each decks himself in his own fash-ion with nuptial extravagances.

The handsome Cockchafer appears at the summer solstice, almost simultaneously with the first Cicadæ.[1] His punctual advent gives him a place in the entomological calendar,

[1] Cf. *The Life of the Grasshopper:* chaps. i to v.—*Translator's Note.*

which is no less regular than that of the seasons. When the longest days come, those days which seem endless and gild the harvest, he never fails to hurry to his tree. The Midsummer bonfires, reminiscent of the festivals of the sun, which the children kindle in the village streets, are no more punctual in date. At this season, every evening, in the gloaming, if the weather be still, the Cockchafer comes to visit the pine-trees in the enclosure. I follow his evolutions with my eyes. With a silent, impetuous flight, the males especially veer to and fro, displaying their great antennary plumes; they make for the branches where the females await them; they fly back and forth, visible as dark streaks against the pallor of the sky, from which the last remnants of daylight are fading. They settle, take flight again and resume their busy rounds. What do they do up there, evening after evening, during the fortnight of the festival?

The thing is evident: they are wooing the ladies and they continue to pay their respects until night has fallen. Next morning, both males and females commonly occupy the lower branches. They lie singly motionless, indifferent to passing events. They do not

The Pine Cockchafer

avoid the hand put out to seize them. Hanging by their hind-legs, most of them nibbling a pine-needle, they slumber drowsily, with the morsel, in their mouths. When twilight returns, they resume their frolics.

To watch these frolics in the tops of the trees is hardly possible; let us try to watch them in captivity. I collect four couples in the morning and place them in a roomy cage, with a few twigs of pine. The spectacle hardly comes up to my expectations. This is because they are deprived of the power of flight. At most, from time to time, a male approaches his coveted bride; he spreads the leaves of his antennæ and shakes them with a slight quiver, perhaps to discover if he is welcome; he shows off, exhibiting his antlered beauty. It is a useless display: the female does not budge, as though insensible to these demonstrations. Captivity has sorrows that are hard to overcome. More than this I could not see. Pairing, it seems, must take place during the later hours of the night, so that I have missed the propitious moment.

One detail in particular interested me. The Pine-chafer possesses a musical instrument. Male and female are similarly gifted. Does the suitor make use of his faculty as a means of seduction and appeal? Does the other answer her lover's strophe with a similar strophe? That this happens under normal conditions, amidst the branches, is highly probable; but I should not care to say so for certain, having never heard anything of the kind among the pine-trees or in the cage.

The sound is produced by the tip of the abdomen, which, with a gentle movement, alternately rises and falls, rubbing its rearmost segments against the hinder edge of the wing-cases, which are held motionless. There is no special appliance on the rubbing surface nor on the surface rubbed. The magnifying-glass searches in vain for minute ridges such as might produce a note. On either hand all is smooth. How then is the sound produced?

Moisten the tip of a finger and run it over a strip of glass, over a window-pane: you will obtain a fairly well-sustained sound, not unlike that emitted by the Cockchafer. Better still: use a bit of india-rubber to rub the glass with and you will obtain a pretty faithful reproduction of the noise made by the insect. If the musical rhythm is well preserved, the imitation might deceive anybody.

Well, in the Cockchafer's apparatus, the pad of the finger-tip and the bit of india-rubber are represented by the softness of the moving abdomen and the window-pane by the plate of the wing-cases, a thin, rigid plate eminently capable of vibration. The Cockchafer's musical instrument is thus one of the simplest.

A small number of other Beetles are endowed with the same privilege. These include the Spanish Copris and the truffle-eating Bolboceras.[1] Both make a sound by means of slight oscillations of the abdomen, which gently grazes the hinder edge of the wing-cases.

The Cerambyx-beetles have another method, likewise based on friction. The Great Capricorn, for instance, moves his corselet over its junction with the thorax. There is here a large cylindrical projection which fits tightly into the cavity of the corselet and forms a joint which is at the same time powerful and mobile. This projection is surmounted by a convex surface,

[1] For this Beetle cf. *The Life of the Fly:* chap. xviii.—*Translator's Note.*

shaped like an heraldic scutcheon, perfectly smooth and absolutely devoid of any sort of fluting. This is the musical-box.

The edge of the corselet, itself smooth inside, rubs over this surface, passing to and fro with a rhythmical movement and thus creating a sound which is once more like that of a window-pane rubbed with a moistened finger. Still, I am unable to make the dead insect's apparatus sound by moving the corselet myself. Though I hear nothing, I at least feel with my moving fingers the shrill vibration of the surfaces rubbed. A little more and the sound would be audible. What is lacking? The stroke of the bow which the live insect alone is able to supply.

We find the same mechanism in the small Capricorn, *Cerambyx cerdo*,[1] and in the denizen of the willows, the Rose-scented Aromia, *A. moschata*.[2] On the other hand, the Ægosoma and Ergates, mighty Longicorns both, are without the projection fitting into the corselet, or rather possess of it only as much as is strictly necessary to join

[1] Cf. *The Glow-worm and Other Beetles:* chap. viii.— *Translator's Note.*

[2] Also known as the Musk Beetle. The insect emits a strong smell of musk and is found crawling on decaying willows.—*Translator's Note.*

the two parts together. Consequently the two big night-insects are dumb.

Though we are acquainted with the simple mechanism of the Cockchafer's instrument, its employment none the less remains a riddle. Does the insect use it as a means of nuptial appeal? This is likely. Nevertheless, I have not heard the slightest grating on the pines, in spite of all my attention at propitious hours. I have heard nothing either in the cages, where distance formed no obstacle to the hearing.

If we would make the Cockchafer squeak, all that we need do is to take him in our fingers and tease him a little. The sound box works at once and does not cease until we do. What we now hear is not a song but a complaint, a protest against misfortune. It is a singular world in which sorrow is translated by couplets and joy by silence.

The other scrapers of the abdomen or corselet behave in like fashion. When surprised upon her pills, at the bottom of her burrow, the mother Copris groans, for a moment bewailing her fate: the Bolboceras, held captive in the hand, protests with a gentle elegy; the Capricorn when caught sets up a desperate grating. All are mute as soon as the danger is past; all likewise persist in their silence when absolutely at rest. I never knew any of the three to sound his instrument apart from the alarm to which I subjected them.

Others, supplied with highly improved instruments, sing to beguile their solitude, to summon each other to the wedding, to celebrate the joys of life and the festival of the sunshine. Most of these singers are mute in a moment of danger. At the least disturbance, the Decticus[1] shuts up his musical box and veils his dulcimer, on whose notes he was playing with his bow; the Cricket[2] furls the wings which were vibrating above his back.

On the other hand, the Cicada raises a desperate outcry in our fingers; and the Ephippiges[3] bemoans his fate in a minor key. Sorrows and joys are translated into the same tongue, so that it becomes difficult to say for what exact purpose the stridulating organ is intended. When left in peace, does the insect actually celebrate its happiness? When teased, does it bewail its misfortune? Does

[1] Cf. *The Life of the Grasshopper:* chaps. xii. and xiii.—*Translator's Note.*

[2] Cf. *idem:* chaps. xv. and xvi.—*Translator's Note.*

[3] Cf. *idem:* chaps. xiii. and xiv.—*Translator's Note.*

The Pine Cockchafer

it try to overawe its enemies with noise?
Could the sound-apparatus, at the requisite
moment be a means of defence or intimida-
tion? If the Capricorn and the Cicada
made a sound when in danger, then why are
the Decticus and the Cricket silent?

After all, we know next to nothing of the
determining causes of insect phonetics. We
know very little more of the sounds perceived. Do the insect's ears catch the same
sounds as ours do? Is it sensible, in particular, to what we call musical sounds? Without, I may say, any hope of solving this obscure problem, I tried an experiment which
is worth relating. One of my readers, filled
with enthusiasm for what my animals taught
him, sent me a musical box from Geneva,
hoping that it might be useful to me in my
acoustic researches. And it really was so.
Let me tell the story. It will give me the
opportunity of thanking the kind sender of
the present.

The little musical-box has a fairly varied
selection of pieces, all translated into notes
of crystal clearness which should, to my
thinking, attract the attention of an insect
audience. One of the tunes best suited to my

plans is that from *Les Cloches de Corneville*. With this lure shall I secure the attention of a Cockchafer, a Capricorn or a Cricket?

I begin with a Capricorn, the little *Cerambyx cerdo*. I seize the moment when he is courting his mate at a distance. With his delicate antennæ extended motionless, he seems to be making enquiries. Now, melodiously, *Les Cloches de Corneville* ring out: ding-dong-ding-dong. The insect's meditative posture is unchanged. There is not the least tremor, not the least inflexion of the antennæ, the organs of hearing. I renew the attempt, altering the hour and the degree of daylight. My experiments are useless: there is not a movement of the antennæ to denote that the insect pays the least attention to my music.

The same result, with the Pine-chafer, whose antennary leaves retain exactly the same position as when all was silent; the same result with the Cricket, whose tiny, outstretched, thread-like antennæ should vibrate easily under the impact of the sound-waves. My three subjects are absolutely indifferent to my methods of exciting emotion: not one of them gives a hint of feeling any impression whatever.

The Pine Cockchafer

Years ago, a mortar thundering under the plane-tree in which the orchestra of the Cicadæ [1] was performing did not for a moment interrupt or otherwise affect their concert: at a later date, the hullabaloo of a holiday crowd and the crackling of fireworks let off close by failed to disturb the geometry of a Garden Spider working at her web,[2] to-day, the limpid tinkle of *Les Cloches de Corneville* leaves the insect profoundly indifferent, in so far as we are able to judge. Are we to infer deafness? That would be going a great deal too far.

These experiments merely justify our opinion that the insect's acoustics are not ours, even as the optics of its faceted eyes are not to be compared with those of our own. A mechanical toy, the microphone, hears—if I be permitted to say so—that which to us is silence; it would not hear a mighty uproar; it would be thrown out of gear and work imperfectly if subjected to the din of thunder. What of the insect, another, even more delicate toy! It knows nothing of our sounds,

[1] Cf. *The Life of the Grasshopper:* chap. iv.—*Translator's Note.*

[2] Cf. *The Life of the Spider,* by J. Henri Fabre, translated by Alexander Teixeira de Mattos: chap. x.—*Translator's Note.*

whether musical notes or noises. It has those of its own little world, apart from which other sound-waves possess no value.

In the first fortnight of July, the male Pine-chafers observed in the vivarium withdraw to one side, sometimes bury themselves and die quite peacefully, killed by age. The mothers, on the other hand, busy themselves with laying their eggs, or, more accurately, with sowing them. They poke the soil with the tip of their abdomen, shaped like a blunt ploughshare, sinking into it sometimes altogether, sometimes to their shoulders. The eggs, to the number of a score, are laid separately, one by one, in little round cavities the size of a pea. They receive no further attention. They are positively dibbled into the ground.

This method recalls the arachis, the African[1] Leguminosa, which curls its floral peduncles and thrusts its oleaginous seeds with their nutty flavour, underground to germinate. It reminds us too of a plant of

[1] I do not wish to correct the author; but I find that all the books of reference in my possession describe the pea-nut (*Arachis hypogea*) as a native of Brazil and I am inclined to think that African, in the French edition, may be a misprint for American.—*Translator's Note.*

my own country-side, the subterranean or double-fruited vetch (Vicia amphicarpos, DORTH.), which produces two sorts of pods, the first above ground, containing numerous seeds, the second under the surface, containing large seeds, usually no more than two in number. For that matter the two kinds are equal in value and give a similar yield.

Let the soil be moistened and everything is ready for the germination; the preliminary sowing has been done by the vetch and the arachis themselves. Here the plant vies with the animal in maternal cares: the Pine-chafer does no more than the two Legumonosæ. She sows in the ground and that is all, absolutely all. How far removed we are from the Minotaur, so careful of her family!

The eggs, ovoids blunted at either end, measure four to five millimetres[1] in length. They are a dull white, firm to the touch, as though supplied with a chalky shell copied from that of a Hen's egg. This appearance is deceptive: what remains after the hatching is a delicate, flexible, translucent membrane. The chalky look is due to the con-

[1] .156 to .195 inch.—*Translator's Note.*

tents, which show through. The hatching takes place in the middle of August, a month after the laying.

How shall I feed the grubs and watch them take their first mouthfuls? I go by what I have learnt from the spots frequented by the grown larvæ. I make a mixture of moist sand and the fine detritus of any leaves whatever browned with decay. The new-born grubs thrive in this environment: I see them opening short galleries here and there, seizing on decayed particles and devouring them with every sign of satisfaction, so much so that, if I had the leisure to continue this rearing for the three or four years required, I should certainly obtain larvæ ripe for transformation.

But there is no need to waste my time in rearing them thus: by digging in the fields I obtain the fully developed grub. It is magnificently fat, bent into a hook, a creamy white in front and an earthy brown behind, because of the wallet in which it hoards the stercoral treasure destined later to plaster and cement the cell in which the nymphosis will take place. All these hook-shaped wallet-bearers, Oryctes- and Cetonia-larvæ,

The Pine Cockchafer

Cockchafer- and Anoxia-grubs, are hoarders
of fæcal matter: they reserve in their brown
paunches the wherewithal to build themselves
a lodging when the time comes.

I collect my fat grubs in a sandy soil,
where lean grass-tufts grow, at a great distance from any resinous tree except the cy-
press, which the adult insect does not visit.
The Cockchafer, therefore, after her regulation frolics on the pines, came to this place
from afar to lay her eggs. She feeds frugally on pine-needles; her larva calls for the
remnants of any leaves softened by underground putrefaction. This is why the nuptial paradise is deserted.

The larva of the Common Cockchafer, the
White Worm, a voracious nibbler of tender
roots, is the scourge of our crops; that of the
Pine Cockchafer seems to me to work hardly
any havoc. Decayed rootlets, decomposing
vegetable remains, are all that it needs. As
to the adults, they browse upon the green
pine-needles, without abusing their privilege.
If I were a land-owner, I should not trouble
my head about their devastations. A few
mouthfuls taken from the immense store of
leaves, a few pine-needles robbed of their

points, are not a serious matter. Let us leave the Pine Cockchafer alone. He is an ornament of the balmy twilight, a pretty jewel of the summer solstice.

CHAPTER X

THE VEGETARIAN INSECTS

ALONE of living creatures, civilized man knows how to eat, by which I mean to say that he treats the affairs of the stomach with a certain pomp and circumstance. He is an expert cook and an artist in delicate sauces. He celebrates his meals with luxurious plate and crockery. He officiates at table like a high-priest; he practises rites and ceremonies. At his banquets he calls for music and flowers, that he may masticate his portion of dead flesh in splendour.

Animals do not display these eccentricities. They merely feed, which, after all, may very well be the true means of avoiding deterioration. They take nourishment; and that, for them, is enough. They eat to live, whereas many of us live, above all, to eat.

Man's stomach is a pit in which all things edible are engulfed. The stomach of the vegetarian insect is a fastidious laboratory to which nothing but appointed mouthfuls are allowed to find their way. Each guest at the vegetarian banquet has its plant, its fruits, its pod, its seed, which it eagerly exploits, disdaining other victuals, though they may be of equal value.

The carnivorous insect, on the other hand, has no narrow specialities and devours any kind of flesh. The Golden Carabus finds the caterpillar, the Mantis, the Cockchafer, the Earthworm, the Slug or any other kind of game to his taste. The Cerceres collect, for their grubs, bags of Weevils or Buprestes, without distinction of species. The Bruchus,[1] on the other hand, will touch nothing but her pea or her bean; the Golden Rhynchites [2] only her sloe; the Spotted Larinus [3] only the sky-blue ball of her little thistle; the Nut-weevil [4] only her filbert; the Iris-weevil [5] only the capsule of the yellow water iris. And so with other insects. The vegetarian is a short-sighted specialist; the meat-eater an emancipated generalizer.

[1] For the Pea-weevil and the Haricot-weevil, cf. *The Life of the Weevil*, by J. Henri Fabre, translated by Alexander Teixeira de Mattos: chaps. xi. to xiii.—*Translator's Note.*

[2] For the Sloe-weevil, cf. *idem*: chap. x.—*Translator's Note.*

[3] Cf. *idem*: chap. ii.—*Translator's Note.*

[4] Cf. *idem*: chap. vi.—*Translator's Note.*

[5] Cf. *idem*: chap. xiv.—*Translator's Note.*

The Vegetarian Insects

Some years ago, with a success which delighted the observer that I am, I changed the diet of various carnivorous larvæ. To those which lived on Weevils I gave Locusts; to those which lived on Locusts I gave Flies. My nurslings unhesitatingly accepted the food unknown to their race and were none the worse for it; but I would not undertake to rear a caterpillar with the first sort of leaves that came to hand: it would starve sooner than touch them.

Animal matter having undergone a more thorough refinement than vegetable substances, enables the stomach to pass from one dish to another without gradually becoming accustomed to each, whereas vegetable food, being comparatively refractory, calls for an apprenticeship on the part of the consumer. To turn Sheep's flesh into Wolf's flesh is an easy matter: a few minor transmutations are enough; but to make mutton out of grass is a complicated process of digestive chemistry, for which the ruminant's four stomachs are none too many. The carnivorous insect is able to vary its diet, all sorts of game being of equal value.

Vegetable food involves other conditions. With its starches, oils, essences and spices and often with its poisons, each plant tried would be a perilous innovation, to which the insect, repelled by the first mouthfuls, would never consent. How greatly preferable to these dangerous novelties is the invariable dish consecrated by ancient custom! This, no doubt, is why the vegetarian insect is faithful to its plant.

How is this division of the earth's abundance among its consumers effected? We can hardly hope to understand the problem; it is too far beyond our methods of research. The most that we can do is, by experimental methods, to explore this corner of the unknown a little, to seek to discover how far the insect's diet is fixed and to note its variations, if any. This will give us data which the future will employ to carry the problem farther.

Towards the end of the autumn, I had placed in the vivarium two couples of the Stercoraceous Geotrupes, with an ample heap of provender obtained from the Mules. I had no plans as regards my captives; I had put them there because it was an old habit of mine never to lose an opportunity. Chance had set them within my reach; chance would do the rest.

The Vegetarian Insects

With the sumptuous provision which I had bestowed upon them, the Geotrupes had had plenty wherewith to attend to their domestic affairs. They were overlooked all the winter, without any further intervention on my part. On the approach of spring, curiosity impelled me, in a leisure moment, to inspect them. It had been raining as hard through the sides of the cage, which consisted of a metal trellis, as it had in the streets; and, as the water could not trickle away through the wooden floor, the soil in the vivarium had turned to mud.

The sausages of food prepared by the parents were numerous, in spite of everything, but in a shocking state. Soaked by the rain, drenched to the very centre by continual infiltration, they fell into fragments if I moved them. Nevertheless, each contained, in the tattered chamber beneath it, an egg laid about the end of autumn; and this egg, spared by the ice-cold mud of winter, was so plump, so healthy and glossy, that an imminent hatching seemed evident.

What shall I give the grubs when they come out? I dare not count on the remnants of the regulation sausages, reduced to bales of fibre by the rains. As well give the new-born larvæ an old rope's-end. What is to be done? We will resort to a crazy artifice and serve a dish of our own invention, one absolutely unknown to the Geotrupes.

The mess prepared for my larvæ is made of leaves decaying on the ground: hazel-, cherry-, mulberry-, elm-, quince-leaves and others. I steep them in water to soften them and then shred them like fine-cut tobacco. The egg is placed at the bottom of a test-tube; and I pack a column of my vegetable mince-meat on the top. For purposes of comparison, other eggs are similarly lodged, but with a thankless ration of the normal preserves soaked by the rains.

Hatching occurs during the first week in March. I have before my eyes, when it leaves the egg, the larva which astonished me so greatly when I first realized, many years ago, that it was a cripple. In once more referring to this strange abnormality, I will confine myself to a few words on the subject of the head, which is remarkably bulky, swollen as it is by the motor muscles of the mandibular shears with broad, flat blades, notched at the tip and bearing a strong spur at the base. It is enough to see this dental armoury to recognize the new-born grub as one that will not object to tackling ligneous fibres. With such a mincing-machine, a bit of straw must be a luxury.

I watch the grubs taking their first mouthfuls. I expected to see them hesitating, searching uneasily through these unaccustomed victuals, such as no Geotrupes, it seems to me, can ever have used. Nothing of the sort: this eater of dung-sausages accepts the dead-leaf-sausages off-hand and so enthusiastically that I am convinced at the first trial of the success of my queer experiment.

The grub finds before it, to begin with, the main nerve of a leaf. It seizes it, turns it over and over with its palpi and fore-legs and then gently nibbles one end of it. The whole of it goes down. Other morsels follow, large or small indifferently. There is no picking and choosing: what the mandibles encounter they crunch. And this goes on indefinitely, always with an unimpaired appetite, so that the insect attains the perfect stage without a check. When the back is black as ebony and the belly an amethystine violet, I set my Geotrupes at liberty. I am filled with amazement by what he has taught me.

An inverse experiment was essential. A

Dung-beetle thrives on rotten leaves; shall I be equally successful in rearing an eater of vegetable refuse on dung? From the heap of dead leaves accumulated in a corner of the garden for mould, I obtain a dozen half-grown larvæ of the Golden Cetonia. I install them in a glass jar, with no other food than Mule-droppings which have acquired the proper consistency by a few days' exposure to the air on the high-road. The stercoral ration is welcomed by the future rose-dweller. I cannot see any signs of hesitation or repugnance. When half-dry, the Mule's fibrous scraps are consumed as readily as the leaves brown with decay. A second jar contains larvæ fed in the normal fashion. There is no difference between the two groups in the matter of appetite and healthy looks. In both cases the metamorphosis is properly accomplished.

This double success gives food for thought. Certainly the Cetonia-grub would have nothing to gain if it thought fit to abandon its heap of dead leaves in order to exploit the Mule-droppings in the road; it would be leaving inexhaustible abundance, pleasant moisture and perfect security in exchange for a scanty, perilous diet, trampled underfoot by the passers-by. It will not commit this act of folly, however alluring the bait of a new dish.

It is not the same thing with the larva of the Geotrupes. In the open fields, the droppings of beasts of burden, without being scarce, are not by any means to be met with everywhere. They are found chiefly on the roads, which, encrusted with macadam, offer an insuperable obstacle to burrowing. On the other hand, half-rotten dead leaves accumulate everywhere in inexhaustible quantities. What is more, they abound on loose soil, which is easily excavated. If they are too dry, there is nothing to prevent their being carried down to such a depth that the moisture of the soil will give them the requisite pliability. An insect is not a Geotrupes, an earth-borer, for nothing. A silo sunk a few inches deeper than the ordinary burrows would make an excellent steeping-vat.

Since the Geotrupes-grubs thrive on a column of rotten leaves, as my experiments have proved, it would seem that the maker of dung-sausages would gain greatly by slightly modifying her trade and substituting fermented leaves for stercoral matter. The race would be the better for the change and would become more numerous, since there would be plenty of food in perfectly safe places.

If the Geotrupes does nothing of the kind, if it has never even attempted to do so, apart from my artificial methods of rearing, it is because the regimen is not determined merely by the appetites of the consumers. Economic laws regulate the diet and each species has its portion, in order that nothing shall be left unused in the treasury of unorganizable matter.

Let us consider a few examples. The Death's-head Hawk-moth (*Acherontia atropos,* LINN.) has the leaves of the potato for her caterpillar's portion. She is a foreigner, who seems to have come from America together with her food-plant. I have tried to rear her caterpillar on various plants belonging, like the potato, to the family of the Solanaceæ. Henbane, datura and tobacco were obstinately refused, despite the acute hunger displayed when the normal food was served.

The violent alkaloids with which these plants are saturated may perhaps explain this refusal. We will therefore keep the true genus *Solanum* and we will replace the too active poisons by solanin, which is not so virulent. The leaves of the tomato (*Solanum lycopersicum*), the egg-plant (*S. melongena*), the black-berried nightshade (*S. nigrum*), the orange-berried nightshade (*S. villosum*), a native of New Zealand, and the common bittersweet of our country-sides (*S. dulcamara*) are, on the other hand, accepted with the same relish as the potato.

These contradictory results leave me perplexed. Since the caterpillar of the Death's-head Hawk-moth requires food flavoured with solanin, why are certain species of the same genus *Solanum* gluttonously devoured and others refused? Can it be because the dose of solanin is unequal, being weaker here and more abundant there? Or are there other reasons? I am utterly at a loss.

The magnificent caterpillar of the Spurge Hawk-moth, *La Belle,* as Réaumur calls it, knows nothing of these inexplicable preferences. It welcomes any species whose wounds exude the sap of the tithymals, the white milky liquid with the fiery flavour. In my neighbourhood it is often found on the tall spurge of these parts, *Euphorbia characias;* but it is just as happy on smaller species, such as the narrow notch-leaved spurge (*Euphorbia serrata*) and Gerard's spurge (*E. Gerardiana*).

Under my bell-jars it thrives on the first spurge that comes to hand. Anything except these caustic foods, which no other caterpillar would accept, it abhors. It turns away in disdain from the insipid lettuce of our gardens, from peppermint, from the Cruciferæ, rich in sulphurous juices, the caustic ranunculus and other more or less highly flavoured plants. It will have nothing but the spurge, whose milky sap would corrode any gullet but its own. An insect that can feed with pleasure on such acrid fare must obviously be predisposed that way.

For that matter, consumers devoted to pungent flavours are not scarce. The grub of *Brachycerus algirus* is as fond of aioli as the Provençal peasant; it thrives and grows fat in a clove of garlic, without other nourishment.

What is more, I have found the larvæ of I know not what insect on *Nux vomica*, the terrible poison with which our municipal authorities flavour the sausages used for destroying Wolves and stray dogs. These strychnine-eaters have certainly not accus-

tomed themselves by degrees to this terrible
diet: they would perish at the first mouthful, if they had not a specially constructed
stomach at their service.

This exclusive taste for such or such a
vegetable, sometimes harmless and sometimes poisonous, has many exceptions. Some
vegetarian insects are omnivorous. The de-
structive Locust nibbles every green thing;
our common Grasshoppers eat the tips of any
sort of grass without distinction. Kept in
a cage to divert the children, the Field
Cricket feasts on a leaf of lettuce or endive,
new foodstuffs that help it to forget the
tough grasses of his meadows.

In April, on the green banks by the road-
side, we meet with squads of an ugly, fat,
bronze-black creature, which, when we tease
it, plays the Tortoise, shrinking into a ball.
It walks heavily on six feeble legs, while the
end of the intestine, becoming a supplemen-
tary foot, acts as a lever and pushes it forward. It is the larva of a large black Chrysomela (*Timarcha tenebricosa*, FAB.), an unpleasant Beetle which, in self-defense, dis-
gorges an orange spittle.

I amused myself last spring by following a
flock of these larvæ to their grazing-grounds.

The favourite plant was one of the Rubia-
ceæ, the cheese-rennet (*Galium verum*), in
the stage of young shoots. Various other
plants were eaten no less readily on the way,
including especially Cichoriaceæ such as
Pterotheca nemansensis, Chondrilla jubcea
or gum-succory, and cut-leaved podospermum
(*P. laciniatum*), and Leguminosæ such as
Medicago falcata, or yellow medick and *Tri-
folium repens,* or white clover. The acrid
flavours did not in the least discourage the
flock. A Gerard's spurge was met with,
trailing its flower on the ground. A few
larvæ stopped and nibbled the tender tops as
eagerly as the clover. In short, the fat crippled larva varies its meal greatly.

Examples abound of insects equally omnivorous of vegetable substances; there is no
need to linger over them. Let us pass on to
the exploiters of woody materials. The
larva of *Ergates faber* lives exclusively in decayed pine-stumps; the hideous caterpillar of
the Moth inappropriately known as the Cossus eats into old willow-trees, in company
with the Ægosoma.

These two are specialists.

The lesser Capricorn, *Cerambyx cerdo*, en-
trusts her grubs to the hawthorn, the sloe,

the apricot-tree and the cherry-laurel, all of
which trees or shrubs belong to the family of
the Rosaceæ. She varies her domain a
little, while remaining faithful to woody veg-
etation characterized by a faint flavour of
prussic acid.

The Zeuzera, or Leopard-moth, a large
and beautiful white Moth with blue spots, is
more general. She is the scourge of most
of the trees and shrubs in my enclosure. I
find her caterpillar chiefly in the lilac-tree;
also in the elm, the plant-tree, the quince, the
guelder-rose, the pear-tree and the chestnut.
In these, always working upwards, it bores
itself straight galleries which turn a branch
the thickness of a good-sized bottle-neck into
a fragile sheath soon broken by the winter
wind.

To return to the specialists: the Shagreen
Saperda exploits the black poplar and accepts
nothing else, not even the white poplar; the
Spotted Saperda has the elm for its domain;
the Scalary Saperda is faithful to the dead
cherry-tree.[1] The Great Capricorn lodges
her grubs in the oak, sometimes the English
oak and sometimes the evergreen oak, or ilex.

[1] For the Saperda-beetles cf. *The Glow-worm and
Other Beetles:* chap. viii.—*Translator's Note.*

More Beetles

This last Beetle, being easily reared with slices of pear for food and sticks of wood in which to establish her family, lends herself to an experiment of some interest.

I collect the eggs which the mother's pointed, groping oviduct has slipped into the irregular crevices of the bark. The number obtained enables me to make a variety of tests. Will the new-born larvæ accept the first wood that offers after they are hatched. That is the problem.

I select freshly-cut billets measuring two or three fingers'-breadths in diameter. They include the ilex, elm, lime, robinia, cherry, willow, elder, lilac, fig, laurel and pine. To avoid falls, which would confuse the newborn grubs if they had to wander about in search of the spot at which to bore, I do my best to imitate the natural conditions. The mother Capricorn lodges her eggs, one at a time, here and there in the fissures of the bark, fixing them with a thin varnish. I cannot gum the eggs in this way: my glue would perhaps endanger the vitality of the egg; but I can resort to the firm support of a furrow. With the point of a penknife I make this furrow, that is to say, a tiny cleft into which the egg sinks half-way. This precaution succeeds admirably.

In a few days the eggs hatch without falling off, each at the spot decided by the point of my penknife. I watch in amazement the first wriggles of the feeble little creature's body, the first strokes of its plane, as it attacks the thankless material, the bark and the wood, still dragging its white egg-shell behind it. By the following day, each grub has disappeared beneath a fine sawdust, the result of the work accomplished. The mound is still very small, matching the weakness of the excavator. Let us leave the grub at work. For a fortnight we see the mound grow bigger and bigger, until it is almost the size of a pinch of snuff. Then everything stops. The amount of sawdust does not increase, except in the oak-billet.

This activity at the outset, which is everywhere the same, in media differing so greatly in aroma and flavour, would lead us to suppose, at first thoughts, that the young Cerambyx is endowed with a highly complaisant stomach and can feed on the fig-tree, oozing with acrid milk, the laurel, aromatic with essential oils, and the pine, saturated with resin, as well as on the oak, seasoned with tannin. Reflection persuades us that we are mistaken. The little creature is not engaged in eating: it is toiling to make itself a deep lodging in which it can feast in peace.

When examined through the lens, the saw-dust confirms our theory: this dust has not passed through the digestive canal; it has played no part in feeding the grub. It is only so much meal, crumbled by the man-dibles, and nothing more.

When appetite has come and the requisite depth has been reached, the grub at last be-gins to eat. If it finds the traditional food ready to its teeth, the sap-wood of the oak, with its astringent flavour, it gorges itself and proceeds to digest. If it finds nothing of the sort, it abstains from eating. This is certainly the reason why the heap of sawdust grows larger on the billet of oak but remains indefinitely stationary on the others.

What do they do in their little galleries, these grubs subjected to a strict fast in the absence of suitable victuals? In March, six months after the hatching, I look into the matter. I split the billets. There they are, the little grubs, no larger, but still lively, swaying their heads to and fro if I disturb them. This persistence of life in such puny creatures deprived of food rouses our astonishment. It reminds us of the grubs of the Attelabus-beetle, which, subjected to the drought of summer in their little kegs made of a strip of oak-leaf, cease eating and slumber, half-dead, for four or five months, until the autumn rains have softened their food.

When I myself produced rain, a thing not beyond my power, so far as the needs of a grub are concerned, when I softened the rigid kegs and made them edible by a brief immersion in water, the recluses used to return to life, begin to eat again and continue their larval development without further check. Similarly, after six months' fasting in the heart of inacceptable sticks, the Capricorn grubs would have recovered their strength and activity if I had removed them and put before them a freshly-cut billet of oak. I did not do it, so certain did the success of the experiment appear.

I had other schemes in view. I wished to learn how long this arrested life could be prolonged. A year after the hatching, I examined my specimens again. This time I have gone too far. All the grubs are dead, reduced to dark brown granules; only those in the oak are alive and already well-grown. The experiment is conclusive; the Great Capricorn has the oak for her domain; any other tree is fatal to her grub.

Let us recapitulate these details, to which it were easy to add indefinitely. Among the vegetarian insects are some that are omnivorous, by which we mean that they are able to feed on a great variety of plants, but not on all indifferently: that goes without saying. These consumers of miscellaneous foodstuffs are in the minority. The other specialize, some more and others less strictly. One guest at the great banquet of the animal world requires a vegetable family, a group, a genus flavoured with certain alkaloids; another needs a given plant, sometimes faintly and sometimes highly flavoured; a third demands a seed, apart from which nothing is of use to it; and others require their pod, bud, or blossom, their bark, root or bough respectively. So it is with one and all. Each insect has its exclusive tastes, narrowly limited, to the point of refusing the close equivalent of the thing accepted.

Lest we lose our way in the inextricable throng at the entomological banquet let us consider separately our two Capricorns, *Cerambyx heros* and *C. cerdo*. No two creatures could be more alike than these two long-horned Beetles; the lesser is the very picture of the greater. Let us also consider the three Saperdæ mentioned above. They are the same shape, as though they had been turned out of similar moulds, so much so that we should confound them if differences of size and above all of colour did not proclaim them to be of separate species.

The theorists tell us that our two Capricorns and their congeners spring from a common stock, ramified in various directions by the action of the centuries. In the same way, our three Saperdæ and the others are variations of a primitive type. The ancestors of the Capricorns, the Saperdæ and the Longicorns in general are in their turn descended from a remote precursor, who herself was descended from etc., etc. One more plunge into the darkness of the past and we shall soon reach the origins of the zoological series. What begins at all? The Protozoon. How? With a drop of albumen. The whole succession of living creatures has gradually proceeded from this first clot of protoplasm.

As an effort of the imagination, this is magnificent. But the observable facts, which alone are worthy of admission to the stern records of science, the facts corroborated by experiment, cannot keep pace with the Protozoon. They tell us that, as food is the primordial factor of life, digestive capacities should be handed down by atavistic inheritance even more than are the length of the antennæ, the colour of the wing-cases and other details of quite secondary importance. To bring about the present state of affairs, in which the diet is so varied, the precursors must have eaten a little of everything. They ought to have bequeathed to their descendants an omnivorous regimen, which is a notable cause of prosperity.

A common origin would inevitably lead to a common diet. Instead of this, what do we see? Each species has its narrowly limited tastes, which have no reference to the tastes of the cognate species. If they are related through a common ancestry, it is absolutely impossible to understand why, of our two Capricorns, one is allotted the oak and the other the hawthorn and the cherry-laurel; why, of our three Saperdæ, the first demands the black poplar, the second the elm and the third the dead cherry-tree. This gastric independence loudly proclaims independence of origin. And simple common sense, not always welcome to the adventurous theorists, is of the same opinion.

CHAPTER XI

THE DWARFS

A PROVENÇAL proverb says:
*"Chasque toupin trobo sa cubercello;
Chasque badan, sa badarello."*

It is true; every pot finds its lid, every Jack his Jill. The hunchbacked, the blind, the bandy-legged, the physically or morally deformed: one and all have their attractions which render them acceptable in certain eyes.

Insects too, no less than men and stewpans, always find their natural complement, though it mate the faultless with the faulty. Of this *Minotaurus Typhœus* furnishes a splendid example. The hazards of excavation present me with a curious couple, keeping house at the bottom of a burrow. The female calls for no special remark: she is just a handsome matron. But the male! What a sorry creature, what an abortion! The middle point of his trident is reduced to a mere spiked granule; those at the side come just level with the eyes, whereas in normal subjects they reach the extreme point of the head. I measure the little beggar. His length is twelve millimetres [1] instead of eighteen, [2] the ordinary size. According to these figures, the dwarf is barely a quarter of the usual bulk.

In an earlier chapter of the present volume, I mentioned a magnificent male Minotaur who was obstinately refused by the consort whom my experiments had given him. The handsome horn-bearer did not leave the burrow; the other, despite my frequent interventions to restore harmony in the household, deserted her home nightly and sought to set up house elsewhere. I had to give her another partner; the one that I had thrust upon her did not suit her. If the male endowed with a generous stature and trident is often refused, how did the miserable specimen under consideration win the affections of his powerful mate? The unequal associations are doubtless to be explained among the Dung-beetles as among ourselves: love is blind.

Would this ill-assorted pair have bred? And would one part of the family have in-

[1] .468 inch.—*Translator's Note.*
[2] .702 inch.—*Translator's Note.*

herited the noble dimensions of the mother and the other the stunted dimensions of the father? Not possessing, at the moment, a suitable apparatus, that is to say, a tall column of earth held between four planks, I lodged my Beetles in the longest test-tube among my entomological glass-ware, with moist sand and victuals at their disposal.

At first, all went according to rule, the mother digging and the father clearing away the rubbish. A few droppings were stored; then, on reaching the bottom of the test-tube, the couple pined away and died. The layer of sand was not deep enough. Before piling the food-sausage on top of an egg, the pair needed a shaft at least forty inches in depth, whereas they had only some eighteen inches to dig in.

This failure did not put an end to my list of questions. Where did that pigmy spring from? Was he the outcome of a special predisposition, transmitted by heredity? Or was he descended from another dwarf, who himself proceeded from a similar abortion? Was his deficiency merely an accident, which had nothing to do with heredity, an individual littleness not transmissible from father to son? I incline to the theory of an accident. But what sort of accident? I can think of only one liable to diminish the size without injuring the type: I mean, a lack of sufficient food.

We argue thus: animals virtually take shape in a mould whose capacity may be extended in proportion to the amount of molten substance which the crucible pours into it. If this mould receives only the strictly necessary amount, the result is a dwarf. Anything beneath this minimum means death by starvation; anything above it, in doses which increase but are soon limited, means a prosperous life and a normal or slightly larger size. The bulk is decided by *plus* or *minus* quantities of food.

If logic be not a vain delusion, it is therefore possible to obtain dwarfs at will. All that we need do is to diminish the provisions to the lowest limits compatible with the maintenance of life. On the other hand, we cannot hope to make giants by increasing the ration, for a moment comes when the stomach refuses any excess of food. Natural necessities may be likened to a series of rungs of which the one at the top cannot be passed, while it is quite practicable to stand higher or lower on those near the bottom.

First of all we must discover the regular ration. The majority of insects have none. The larva grows up amidst an indeterminate supply of victuals; it eats as it pleases and as much as it pleases, with no other check than its appetite. Others, those most richly endowed in maternal qualities such as the Dung-beetles and the Bees and Wasps, prepare definite rations of preserved food, neither too large nor too small. The Bee stores up in receptacles of clay, cement, resin, cotton or leaf-cuttings just the right amount of honey for a larva's welfare; and, as she knows the sex of the future insects, she puts a little more at the service of the grubs that are to become females and will be slightly larger and a little less at the service of the grubs that are to become males and therefore will be smaller. In like manner, the Hunting Wasps dole out their game according to the sex of the nurslings.

It is now a long time since I did my utmost to upset the mother's wise previsions by taking food from the wealthy grubs to increase the store of the poor. In this way I obtained some slight modifications of size, to which the terms giant and dwarf could not, however, be applied; still less did I succeed in changing the sex, whose determination does not in any way depend upon the quantity of food supplied. The Bees and Wasps are not suited to my present purpose. Their grubs are too delicately constituted. What I want is sturdy stomachs capable of enduring severe ordeals. I shall find them in the Dung-beetles, notably in the Sacred Beetle, whose natural portliness will facilitate our appreciation of any change of bulk.

The big pill-roller calculates the food of her larvæ precisely: each grub has its loaf, kneaded into the shape of a pear. All these loaves are not strictly equal; some are larger and some smaller, but the difference is only minute. Perhaps these slight inequalities are connected with the sex of the nurslings, as among the Bees and Wasps; the females would receive the larger and the males the smaller rations. I did not take any steps to verify this theory. No matter: the fact remains that the Sacred Beetle's pear is, in the mother's opinion, a convenient individual ration. As for me, I can, if I please, alter the size of the loaf, increasing or decreasing it at will. Let us first consider the decrease.

In May, I procure four recent pears, containing the egg in the chamber of the terminal nipple. By making an equatorial section, I cut off the hinder half, in the shape of a large spherical cap; the other half, surmounted by its neck, I retain; and I place the four egg-bearing portions in as many small jars, in which there is no danger of either desiccation or excessive damp.

With these provisions decreased by half, development takes place as usual; then two of the grubs die, apparently the victims of defective hygiene: my jars are not equal to the burrows, with their pleasant moisture. The two others are still in good condition, ever ready to plug with dung the window which I cut through the wall of the cell when I wish to inspect them. At the end of the active period, I find them remarkably small in comparison with those of their fellows who have been left in possession of the whole pear. The effect of insufficient food is already manifest. What will it be in the perfect insect?

In September there emerge from the shells

The Dwarfs

adults such as my hunts in the meadows never yielded, dwarfs, hardly larger than a thumbnail, but correctly shaped in every other respect.

Let me quote some exact figures. Each of them measures nineteen millimetres [1] from the edge of the clypeus to the tip of the abdomen. The smallest specimen in my boxes, as the freedom of the fields made him, measures twenty-six.[2] The products of my experiments, fed upon half rations, are therefore only half the bulk of the normal Beetle chosen from among the smallest. This is also approximately the ratio between the full and the reduced diet. The extensible mould of the organism has reproduced the proportion of the substance at its disposal.

My intervention has just created dwarfs; treatment by starvation has given me abortions. I am not excessively proud of it, though I am glad to have learned by experiment that dwarfishness, at all events in the insects, is not a matter of predisposition and heredity but a mere accident caused by deficient nourishment.

What then had happened to the little Min-

[1] ¾ inch.—*Translator's Note.*
[2] 1 inch.—*Translator's Note.*

otaur who suggested these experiments in starvation? Assuredly a deficiency of food. Though expert in the art of rationing, the mother was unable to complete the sausage over the egg, perhaps because the materials were lacking, or because some inopportune incident interrupted her work; and the grub, scantily fed, though strong enough to withstand a not too rigorous diet, was unable to acquire the wherewithal to provide the adult with the amount of substance needed for the normal size. This seems to be the whole secret of the tiny Minotaur. He was a child of poverty.

While privation reduces the size, it does not follow that unlimited abundance is able to increase it very notably. In vain do I provide the grubs of the Sacred Beetle with an extra allowance of food that doubles or trebles the ration supplied by the mother. My boarders do not attain a growth worth mentioning. As they leave the maternal pears, so do they leave the plentiful messes which my spatula has mixed for them. And this must be so: the appetite has its limits, which, once reached, leave the consumer indifferent to the luxuries of the table. It is not in our power to make giants by means of an excess of food. When the grub has gorged to the required degree, it ceases to eat.

There are nevertheless giants among the Sacred Beetles. I have some that came from Ajaccio and Algeria and measure thirty-four millimetres [1] in length. By comparing this figure with those already given, we see that, if the size of the dwarfs obtained by fasting is represented by the figure 1, that of the Sacred Beetle of the Sérignan district is expressed by 2 and that of the Corsican and African Beetles by 5.

To produce these latter, these giants, it is evident that a more generous diet is needed. Whence comes this increase of appetite? We whet ours with condiments. The insect may well have condiments of its own, for instance, as regards the Sacred Beetle, the pepper of the sea-breezes and the mustard of a generous sun. Such, it seems to me, are the causes which augment the dimensions of the African Scarabæus and reduce those of his Sérignan kinsman. As I have not these two appetizers, the sea and the sun, at my disposal, I give up the idea of making giants by an excess of victuals.

[1] .326 inch.—*Translator's Note.*

More Beetles

Let us now try the larvæ which, not being rationed by the mother, have unlimited abundance at their disposal. Among them are the larvæ of *Cetonia floricola*, HERBST, living in heaps of decomposing leaves. I shall certainly never obtain giants from these by resorting to the artifice of a copious diet! In a corner of my garden they swarm in a heap of rotten leaves, where they find the wherewithal to satisfy their gluttonous appetites to the full, without having to hunt for it; and yet I never find an adult whose dimensions are ever so little exaggerated. To make him exceed the usual proportions it is probable that better climatic conditions are necessary, as in the case of the Sacred Beetle, conditions of which I know nothing and which, moreover, I should be unable to realize. Only one experiment lies within my power, that of starvation.

At the beginning of April, I take three batches of larvæ of *Cetonia floricola* chosen from among those most fully developed and therefore liable to undergo their transformation during the course of the summer. At this April season the great hunger sets in which doubles the size of the grub and amasses the reserves needed for the elabora-

The Dwarfs

tion of the adult. The three batches are installed in large tin boxes, carefully closed, in which there is no danger of too rapid desiccation.

The first batch consists of twelve grubs, which are given an abundance of food, renewed as the need arises. My prisoners could not be better off in the heap of leaf-mould, their favourite resort.

Side by side with this gastric paradise, a second tin, a very inferno of starvation, receives a dozen larvæ kept absolutely without food. It is furnished—as, for that matter, are the others—with a litter of droppings, enabling the famished creatures to wander about or bury themselves at will.

Lastly, the third batch, likewise twelve in number, receives from time to time a scanty pinch of rotten leaves, enough at most to beguile their mandibles for a moment.

Three or four months go by and, when the torrid heats of July have come, the first tin gives me the perfect insect. Its development has been accomplished without a check: the twelve grubs are succeeded by twelve magnificent Cetoniæ, resembling at all points those who sip and slumber in the roses when the spring comes. This result convinces me that the defects attaching to rearing in confinement have nothing to do with what remains to be told.

The second tin, in which strict abstinence is enforced, provides me with two chrysalids, whose diminished size indicates the presence of dwarfs. I wait until the middle of September to open these caskets, which remained closed when those in the first tin burst, two months ago. Their persistent refusal to split open is explained: each of them contains nothing but a dead larva. Absolute starvation was too much for the grubs' endurance. Of the twelve kept without food, ten shrivelled up and eventually died; only two managed to wrap themselves in a shell, by gluing the droppings round about in the usual way. This was their last effort. The two grubs, incapable of performing the consummate labour of the nymphosis, perished in their turn.

Lastly, in the third tin, where victuals were very sparingly provided, eleven grubs out of twelve died, worn out with privation. One only has enclosed itself in a cocoon, which is correctly made but very much reduced in size. If there is a living insect within, it can only be a dwarf. In the middle of September, I open the cabin myself, for there is nothing yet, at this late period, to announce an impending natural fracture.

The contents fill me with delight. They consist of a Cetonia, alive and kicking, all brilliant with metallic gleams and streaked with a few white stripes, like those of the species who have developed freely in the great heap of earth-mould. The shape and costume are not altered in any respect. As for size, that is another matter. I have before my eyes a pigmy, a little gem more exquisite than any collector ever found on the blossoming hawthorns. From the edge of the clypeus to the tips of the wing-cases this creature of my artificial devices measures thirteen millimetres,[1] no more. The insect would have measured twenty millimetres[2] if the grub had been properly fed, far away from my famine-stricken tins. From these figures we deduce that the dwarf's bulk is about one-fourth of what it would have become normally, without my interference.

Of the twenty-four larvæ subjected, during three or four months, some to an absolute fast and others to a diet of meagre

---

[1] ½ inch.—*Translator's Note.*
[2] ¾ inch.—*Translator's Note.*

mouthfuls administered at long intervals, one only reached the adult form. The bad effects of abstinence are far-reaching and the pigmy still feels them. Though the season when the caskets should have split had long gone by, he had made no attempt to free himself. Perhaps he had not the necessary strength. I myself had to break open the cell.

Now that he is free and revelling in the light, he kicks and struggles and starts running, if I tease him at all; but he prefers to rest. One would think that he was overwhelmed by an insurmountable lassitude. I know how gluttonously the Cetoniæ attack fruit at this warm season, gorging themselves upon the sweet pulp. I give my dwarf a piece of juicy fig. He does not touch it, preferring to doze. Is it not yet time for him to eat, after his forcible liberation? Was the recluse intended to spend the winter in his shell before tasting the joys but also risking the dangers of the outer world? It may be so.

At any rate this curious little creature, the small Cetonia, reduced to one-fourth of the regulation size, repeats what the Sacred Beetle but now taught us in a less conclusive fashion, that, among the insects and very likely elsewhere, dwarfishness is the result of incomplete nutrition and not in any way the effect of predisposition.

Let us suppose an impossible case, or at least one extremely difficult to realize; let us imagine that, having obtained by starvation a few couples of Cetoniæ, we were able to keep them alive under favourable conditions. Would they found a family? And what would their offspring be like? The insect, in all probability, would not reply to our question, even though entreated by long perseverance; but the plant answers us readily.

On the paths in my two acres of pebbles, at spots where a little moisture lingers, there grows in April a familiar plant, the whitlow grass (*Draba verna*, LIN.). There is but little nourishment in this ungrateful trodden soil, hard with gravel, and the whitlow grass may be regarded as the equivalent of my famished Cetoniæ. From a flat pattern of sickly leaves rises a single stem, no thicker than a hair, barely an inch in height and with few ramifications or none, which nevertheless ripens its silicles, often reduced to one alone. Here, in short, I have a little garden of dwarf plants, the children of dearth.

More Beetles

My experiments in starvation were far from obtaining such results with the Sacred Beetle and the Cetonia.

I collect the seeds from the heads of the sickliest of these plants and sow them in good soil. Next spring, the dwarfishness disappears at once; the direct descendants of the abortive plants produce ample radiating patterns, multiple stalks reaching to a height of four inches or more and numerous ramifications, rich in silicles. The normal condition has returned.

If they had had enough energy to procreate their species, my dwarf insects, resulting from my artifices or from a casual concourse of enfeebling circumstances, would do as much. They would repeat what the whitlow grass has told us: that dwarfishness is an accident which heredity does not hand down, any more than it hands down knock-knees, or bow-legs, or the hunchback's hump or the stump of the one-armed cripple.

CHAPTER XII

SOME ANOMALIES

THE anomalous is that which forms an exception to the rule, which again is based upon an aggregate of concordant facts. An insect has six legs, each ending in a finger. That is the rule. Why six legs and not some other number? Why one finger and not several? Such questions are so obviously inane that they do not even occur to our minds. The rule exists because it does exist; we note it and that is all. We remain in blissful ignorance of the reason for its existence.

Anomalies, on the other hand, make us uncomfortable and upset all our ideas. Why should there be exceptions, irregularities, contradictions of the letter of the law? Does the sign-manual of disorder leave its imprint here and there? Is the shriek of crazy discord heard amid the general harmony? This is a weighty question; and we should do well to look into it a little, though we have little hope of ever solving the problem.

Let us, to begin with, mention a few of these infractions of the rule. Among the strangest that my chance discoveries have submitted to my scrutiny is that of the larva of the Geotrupes. When I made its acquaintance for the first time, the crippled grub had attained very nearly its full growth. One might reasonably ask one's self whether certain hardships endured during its lifetime had not gradually brought about the weakness of the hind-legs and their abnormal position; whether, at all events, the curious deformity might not be explained by the grub's cramped situation in a narrow corridor in the heart of its food-supply.

Today I am better-informed. The Geotrupes' larva does not gradually become lame through straining itself; it is born crippled, there is no doubt of that. I observe its hatching. I watch the new-born grub through my magnifying-glass as it leaves the egg. The hind-legs which the adult Beetle uses as powerful squeezers for pressing the material which he has gathered and making it into sausages are for the moment reduced to the sorriest of appendages, mere useless counterfeits. They lie withered against the larva's back. Bent into a hook, their extremities avoid the ground and turn in towards the insect's back, without furnishing the least support for standing. They are not legs but uncertain attempts, awkward experiments.

The fore-legs, though well-shaped, are of insignificant dimensions. The tiny creature keeps them tucked away under the front of its body, where they serve to hold in position the morsel at which it is nibbling. The middle pair, on the contrary, are long and powerful and well in evidence. Standing up like two stout crutches, they lend stability to the fat, curved paunch, which has a tendency to capsize. When seen from behind, the grub gives the impression of being the most whimsical creature on earth. It is just a pot-belly mounted on a pair of stilts.

What is the object of this curious organization? One can understand the grotesque hump worn by the grub of the Onthophagus, the sugar-loaf knapsack whose weight is constantly overturning the little creature when it tries to change its position. This hump is a storehouse of cement for the construction of the cabin in which the transformation is to take place. But we cannot understand the two withered, misshapen legs of the Geotrupes' grub, which, one would think, would have been very useful if they had grown into serviceable grappling-irons. The grub shifts its position; it climbs up and down inside its tall column of victuals; it moves about in quest of morsels to suit it. Those two neglected supports would make the climbing easier if they were in good condition.

On the other hand, the grub of the Sacred Beetle, confined in a narrow recess, has hardly any need of locomotion. A simple movement of the hinder-part brings within the reach of its mandibles a fresh layer of the victuals to be consumed. No matter: it is blessed with six sound, well-turned legs. The cripple moves to and fro, the lusty athlete is stationary; the limping grub takes its walks abroad, the nimble one sits still. There is no satisfactory way of explaining this paradox.

In the adult form, the Sacred Beetle and his kinsfolk, the Half-spotted Scarab,[1] the broad-necked Scarab [2] and the Pock-marked

[1] Cf. *The Sacred Beetle and Others*: chap. ii.— *Translator's Note*.
[2] Cf. *idem*: chap. viii.—*Translator's Note*.

Some Anomalies

Scarab [1]—the only three that I know—are likewise atrophied: all of them lack the tarsi of the fore-legs. These four witnesses prove to us that this singular mutilation is common to the whole group.

An absurd system of nomenclature has seen fit, in its blindness, to substitute for the ancient and venerable term of Scarabæus that of Ateuchus, meaning weaponless. The inventor of the name was none too well-inspired: there are plenty of other Dung-beetles that have no horny armour, such as the Gymnopleuri,[2] who are so closely allied to the Scarabæi. Since his intention was to designate the genus by calling attention to a characteristic peculiarity, he should have coined a word meaning, "deprived of tarsi on the fore-legs." Only the Sacred Beetle and his kinsfolk, in the whole of the insect-world, could rightly bear that name. This never occurred to the nomenclator; this important detail was apparently unknown to him. He saw the grain of sand and did not notice the mountain: a defect not uncommon among the forgers of names.

For what reasons are the Scarabs' fore-

[1] Cf. *The Sacred Beetle and Others*: chap. iii.—*Translator's Note.*
[2] Cf. *idem:* chap. viii.—*Translator's Note.*
259

legs bereft of that one finger, the five-jointed tarsus, which in itself represents the insect's hand? Why a stump, a docked limb, instead of a fingered extremity, as is the rule every otherwise? One reply suggests itself which at first seems rather plausible. Those zealous pill-rollers push their load backwards, with their head down and their hinder-part in the air; they support themselves on the tips of their fore-legs. The whole effort of the transportation is brought to bear on the extremities of these two levers, which are in constant contact with the rough ground.

A delicate finger, liable to be sprained under such conditions, would be a hindrance, wherefore the pill-maker decided to do without it. How and when was the mutilation effected? Does it occur nowadays, as a workshop accident, during the actual work? No, for you never see a Scarab furnished with tarsi to his fore-legs, however new he may be at his trade; no, for the nymph, lying perfectly at rest in its shell, has fingerless fore-arms like the adult.

The mutilation dates farther back. Suppose we admit that, in the dim and distant ages, a Scarab, owing to some mishap, lost those two inconvenient and almost superfluous fingers. Finding himself all the better for it, he transmitted the fortunate defect to his race by way of an ancestral legacy. Since then, the Scarabs form an exception to the rule that fore-legs have digits like the rest.

This would be an attractive explanation, but there are serious difficulties in the way. We ask ourselves by what curious freak the organism can have elaborated in days long past portions destined to disappear afterwards as too cumbrous. Can the plan of the animal frame be devoid of logic, of foresight? Does it design the structure blindly, at the hazard of conflicting circumstances?

Away with such foolishness! No, the Scarab did not at one time have the tarsi which he lacks to-day; no, he did not lose them as the result of being harnessed upside down when rolling his pill. He is now what he always was. Who says so? Unimpeachable witnesses: the Gymnopleurus and the Sisyphus,[1] themselves enthusiastic pill-rollers. Like the Scarab, they push them backwards, head down; like the Scarab, they support themselves, during their arduous task, on the tips of their fore-legs; and those

[1] Cf. *The Sacred Beetle and Others:* chap. xv.—*Translator's Note.*

legs, notwithstanding their contact with the rough ground, are as perfectly fingered as the others: they possess the delicate tarsi which the Scarab is denied. Then why should the latter prove an exception to what in the others is the rule? How gladly would I welcome a word from the discerning person who could answer my humble question!

My satisfaction would be equally great if I knew why the Iris-weevil's [1] tarsus has a single nail, whereas the other insects have two, set side by side and bent into a hook. Why was one of these two little claws suppressed? Would it not have been useful to the insect? One would think so. The little Weevil thus mutilated is a climber; she clambers up the smooth stems of the iris; she explores the flowers, visiting the lower surface of the petals as well as the upper; she walks upside down on the slippery pods. An extra hook would do much to ensure her steadiness; yet the thoughtless Weevil deprives herself of it, though by law she has a right to the double claw invariably wielded by the others, even in her own long-nosed clan. What then is the secret of the little Iris-weevil's missing finger-nail?

[1] Cf. *The Life of the Weevil:* chap. xiv.—*Translator's Note.*

Some Anomalies

A tiny claw the less, though a serious business where matters of principle are concerned, is after all a detail of no great material value; one needs a lens to perceive the irregularity. But here is something that the eye can see without the aid of the magnifying-glass.

A Locust from the green slopes of the Alps, *Pezzotettyx pedestris*,[1] who dwells on the higher ridges of *Mont Ventoux*,[2] renounces her right to wings of any kind; she reaches the adult stage while preserving the larval formation. The approach of the wedding-day makes her a little handsomer, adds a touch of coral-red to her sturdy thighs and of sky-blue to her shanks; but there all progress stops. She becomes ripe for marriage and maternity without acquiring the power of flying which the other Acridians possess in addition to that of leaping.

Among the hoppers, all endowed with wings and wing-cases, she remains a clumsy pedestrian, as her Latin affix, *pedestris*, informs us. Nevertheless, the cripple bears

[1] *The Life of the Grasshopper:* chap. xvii.—*Translator's Note.*

[2] The highest mountain in the neighbourhood of Sérignan; 6,268 feet. Cf. *The Hunting Wasps:* by J. Henri Fabre, translated by Alexander Teixeira de Mattos: chap. xi.—*Translator's Note.*

on her shoulders a pair of skimpy sheaths which contain the organs of flight, incapable of unfolding. By what curious evolutionary whim is the pretty Locust with the azure legs deprived of the wings and wing-cases of which she carries the germs in two miserable little bundles? She is promised the gift of flight and does not receive it. For no appreciable reason, the wheels of the animal mechanism are arrested.

Stranger still is the case of the Psyches, whose females, unable to become the Moths promised in their early stages, remain caterpillars, or rather change into wallets stuffed with eggs. Wings with gorgeous scales, the supreme prerogative of Moth and Butterfly, are denied them. The males alone achieve the promised shape; they turn into plumed dandies, clad in black velvet, and are excellent flyers. Why does one—and that one the more important—of the sexes remain a wretched little sausage, while the other is made glorious by the metamorphosis?

And now what are we to say of the next, *Necydalis major,* a denizen of the poplar and the willow in his larval state? He is a Longicorn, fairly imposing in size as compared with *Cerambyx cerdo,* the little Capricorn of the hawthorn. When one is a Beetle—and that he assuredly is—one dons wing-cases which form a sheath, enclosing the body and protecting the delicate wings and the soft and vulnerable abdomen. The Necydalis laughs at rules. He wears on his shoulders, by way of wing-cases, two short pieces which make him an inadequate jacket. It really looks as though there were not sufficient stuff to lengthen out the coat and give it a pair of tails capable of covering that which ought to be covered.

Beyond it stretch, entirely unprotected, two large wings reaching to the tip of the abdomen. At first sight, you would think that you had before your eyes some sort of huge, fantastic Wasp. Why, in an actual Beetle, this niggardly provision of wing-cases? Can the material have run short? Was the cost of prolonging the protective sheath begun at the shoulders too great? We stand amazed at such meanness.

What again shall we say of this other Beetle, *Myodites subdipterus?* Her grub establishes itself, I know not how, in the cells of *Halictus zebra* [1] and battens on the nymph

---

[1] A wild Bee. Cf. *Bramble-dwellers and Others,* by J. Henri Fabre, translated by Alexander Teixeira de Mattos: chaps. xii. to xiv.—*Translator's Note.*

that owns the premises. The adult frequents in summer the prickly heads of the field eringo. To look at her, you would take her for a Dipteron, for a Fly, because of her two big wings uncovered by wing-cases. Examine her more closely and you will see that she carries on her shoulders two small scales, all that remains of the suppressed wing-cases. She is yet another who has not known how or rather has not been able to complete the parts of which she carries these absurd rudiments.

An entire group, one of the most numerous among the Beetles, that of the Staphylini, or Rove-beetles, cuts down its wing-cases to a third or a quarter of the normal dimensions. With excessive economy, the insect with the long, wriggling belly makes itself unsightly and goes too scantily clad.

I might continue for a long time to enumerate the deformed, the irregular, the exceptional; the "whys" would follow close upon one another and no reply would be forthcoming. Animals are uncommunicative; plants, when cunningly entreated, lend themselves better to enquiry. Let us consult them on this problem of anomalies; perhaps they will tell us something.

Some Anomalies

The rose-tree sets us this puzzle:

"We are five brothers; two of us have beards, two have none and the fifth has half a beard."

The case has even been stated in a Latin couplet:

Quinque sumus fratres: unus barbatus et alter;
Imberbesque duo; sum semiberbis ego.

Who are the five brothers? None other than the five lobes of the rose's calyx, the five sepals. Let us examine them one by one. We shall find two of them furnished on both edges with leafy or beard-like appendages, which sometimes revert to the original form and expand into folicles similar to those of the leaves proper. Botany in fact teaches us that a sepal is a modified leaf. These are the two brothers with beards.

We shall see two others totally devoid of appendages on either side. These are the two brothers without beards. Lastly, the fifth will show us one bare and one bearded surface. This one represents the brother with half a beard.

These are not casual variations, differing from flower to flower; all the roses present the same arrangement, all have their sepals divided into three classes in the matter of beards. It is a fixed rule, resulting from a law which governs floral architecture, even as the art of a Vitruvius [1] governs our buildings. This law, so elegant in its simplicity, is thus stated in botany: in the quinary order, the most important order of the vegetable world, the flower groups the five portions of a whorl at intervals upon a close spiral, almost equivalent to the circumference of a circle; and this arrangement is so contrived that two turns of the spiral contain the series of five parts.

Having said this, it is easy to construct the plan of the rose, in so far as concerns the calyx. Divide a circumference into five equal parts. At the first dividing-point, place a sepal. Where shall we put the second? It must not be at the second dividing-point, for then the set of five pieces would fill the circumference in a single revolution, instead of in two. We shall place it at the third point and continue in like fashion, each time missing one division. This mode of progress is the only one that brings us back

[1] Marcus Vitruvius Pollio (*fl. sub Augusto*), author of *De Architectura.—Translator's Note.*

to the starting-point after two turns of the spiral.

Let us now give the sepals a base wide enough to provide a tightly closed containing wall. We shall see that the parts on sections 1 and 3 are completely outside the spiral; that the parts on sections 2 and 4 have their two edges fitting under the adjoining sepals; and that, lastly, the part on section 5 has one edge covered and one free. On the other hand, it is manifest that, hampered in their expansion by the petal placed over them, the edges caught under the others cannot send forth their delicate appendages. Hence we have the two bearded sepals at points 1 and 3, the two beardless sepals at points 2 and 4 and the half-bearded sepal at point 5.

This explains the riddle of the rose. The disparity of the five pieces of the calyx, apparently an irrational structure, a capricious anomaly, is really the corollary of a mathematical law, the natural consequence of an immanent algebraical relation. Disorder is eloquent of order; irregularity bears evidence of a ruling principle.

Let us continue our excursion into the realm of the plants. The quinary order allots to the flower five petals arranged in a whorl of perfect accuracy. Well, a good many corollas depart from the normal grouping, as instance the labiate and the personate corollas. In the former, five lobes compose the limb expanding at the end of a tubular portion and represent the five regulation petals. They are arranged in two wide-open lips, one pointing upwards and one downwards. The upper lip has two lobes, the lower three.

The personate corolla likewise is divided into two lips, the upper having two lobes, the lower three; only, the latter is expanded into an arch that closes the entrance to the flower. A pressure of the fingers on the sides opens the two lips, which close again as soon as the pressure ceases. Hence a certain resemblance to the jaws—the *mufle* or *gueule*—of an animal, a resemblance which has earned for the plant in which this formation is most clearly seen, the name of Snapdragon, *muflier* or *gueule-de-loup*. A certain analogy has also been drawn between the appearance of the two thick lips of the snapdragon and the exaggerated features of the masks, or *personæ*, with which the actors in the ancient theatres used to cover their faces to represent the characters whom they were playing. Hence the expression "personate corolla."

The anomaly of the two-lipped corolla entails modifications in the stamens, which have to adapt themselves to the exigencies of the space enclosed, which is narrower at one point and roomier at another. Of the five stamens, one is suppressed, while often leaving a vestige at its base, as a certificate that it was once there. The four others are grouped into two pairs of unequal length, with a tendency to the suppression of the lesser pair.

The sage achieves this suppression. It has only two stamens, those of the longer pair. Moreover, on each of the staminal filaments it preserves only half an anther. According to the rule in the vast majority of cases, an anther consists of two compartments, placed back to back and separated by a slender partition, known as the connective. The sage exaggerates the size of this connective and makes of it the beam of a balance placed crosswise on the filament. At the end of one arm of this beam is the half of an anther, that is to say, a pollen-sac; at the other end is nothing. The whole of the staminal verticil, all save that which is strictly necessary, is sacrificed to the beautiful strangeness of the corolla.

Now why do the Labiatæ, the Personatæ and other vegetable orders present these anomalies which completely disarrange the regular structure of the flower? Let us in this connection venture upon an architectural comparison. The first men who ventured to balance heavy hewn stones over empty space, thereby deserving the proud title of *pontifex*, or bridge-builder, took as the pattern of their fabric the semicircular arch, which rests the thrust of the load on uniform *voussoirs*. The result is strong and majestic, but also monotonous and lacking in elegance.

Next came the pointed arch, which opposes two arcs described from different centres. With the new type, soaring curves, slender ribs and magnificent superstructures are possible. Variety, inexhaustible in its graceful combinations, replaces monotony.

Well, the regular corolla is, so to speak, the semicircular arch of the flower. Whether campanulate, rotate, urceolate, stellate, or of any other shape, it is always a grouping of similar parts around a circumference. The irregular corolla is the ogive, with its wonderful audacities; it lends to the poetry of the flower the admired disorder of all true poetry. The thick-lipped mask of the snap-dragon, the gaping jaws of the sage are every whit as effective as the rosette of the haw-thorn or the sloe. They a⸱e so many chro-matic notes added to the gamut, so many charming variations upon one glorious theme, so many discords that enhance the value of the harmonies. The floral sym-phony gains if interrupted by occasional solos.

The Pedestrian Locust, hopping among the saxifrage amid the lofty summits of the hills, explains his incapacity to fly by reasons of a like order; so does the Staphylinus his skimpy jacket, the Necydalis his short coat, the Myodites her Fly-like aspect. Each after his fashion varies the monotony of the general theme; each strikes a special note in the universal concert. It is not so easy to see why the Scarab abandons his fore-tarsi, why the Iris-beetle has only one claw to her fingers, why the Geotrupes-grub is born mu-tilated. To what are these minute aberra-tions due? Before answering, let us once again take counsel with the plant.

One of the inmates of our hothouses is the *Alstræmeria pelegrina,* or Inca lily, a

native of Peru. This curious plant sets us
a puzzling problem. At the first glance, its
leaves, shaped more or less like those of the
willow, offer nothing that deserves attentive
examination; but look at them more closely.
The leaf-stalk, flattened into a ribbon of
some length, is tightly twisted upon itself;
and the twist is repeated on every one of the
leaves. From one end of the plant to the
other we find this clearly-marked torsion.

Delicately, with the tips of our fingers, let
us re-establish the natural order of affairs
and spread out flat the ribbon of the twisted
leaf-stalk. A surprise awaits us. The un-
twisted ribbon, replaced in its normal position, is upside down; it shows on the top what
ought to be underneath, that is to say, the
pale surface, rich in stomata and deeply
veined; it shows underneath what ought to
be on top, that is to say, the green, smooth
surface, as is the rule with all other plants.

In short, the Inca lily, when we forcibly
restore the natural arrangement by undoing
its torsions, has its leaves upside down.
What was made for the shadow faces the
light, what was made for the light faces the
shadow. In this contrary arrangement, the
functions of the leaves become impossible;

and so the plant, to correct this defective order, twists the necks of all its leaves by the spiral deformation of the leaf-stalks.

The rays of the sun provoke this reversal. If we intervene with our artificial devices, they may undo what they did at first. With the aid of a light prop and a few ligatures, I bend a shoot of the lily and fix it head downwards. As a result of exposure to the sun, the leaf-stalks in a few days' time untwist themselves and become flat ribbons, which turn their smooth, green sides towards the light and their pale, veined surface towards the shade. The torsion has disappeared, the normal direction of the leaves is restored, but the plant is upside down.

In the case of the Inca lily, with its leaves set the wrong way round on the stem, are we confronted with a blunder which the plant, aided by the sun, does its best to correct by twisting its leaf-stalks? Are there such things as organic frivolity, mistakes, the signature of disorder? Is it not rather our ignorance of cause and effect which regards as erroneous what is actually correct? If our knowledge were greater, how many discordant notes would become harmonious! And so the wisest course is to doubt.

More Beetles

Of all the signs which we employ in writing, the one most nearly resembling the idea which it expresses is the note of interrogation. At the bottom, a round speck: the ball of the world. Above it, twisted into a great crozier, is the *lituus* of antiquity, the augur's wand interrogating the unknown. I like to regard this sign as the emblem of science in perpetual colloquy with the how and why of things.

Now, high as it may rise to obtain a better view, this questioning staff is surrounded by a narrow and obscure horizon, which future investigations will replace by other horizons more remote and no less obscure. Beyond all these horizons, laboriously torn asunder, one by one, by the progress of knowledge, beyond all this obscurity, what is there? Assuredly, the broad light of day, the wherefore of the why, the reason of reasons, in short the great x of the world's equation. So says our questioning instinct, ever dissatisfied, never weary; and instinct, which is infallible in the animal domain, should be no less so in the domain of the mind.

So far as lies in my power, I have sought to discern the essential motives of the insect's anomalies. By no means always has the answer brought a firm conviction. And so, to end this chapter, in which so many glimpses remain shrouded in doubt, I set here, plain to see, in the middle of the page, the augur's *lituus*, the note of interrogation:

CHAPTER XIII

THE GOLD BEETLES : THEIR FOOD

AS I write the first lines of this chapter, I think of the Chicago slaughter-yards. Those horrible meat-factories where, in the course of the year, men cut up over a million Bullocks and nearly two million Pigs, which, entering the factory alive, come out at the other end changed into tins of preserved meat, lard, sausages and rolled hams. I think of them because the Carabus, or Ground-beetle, is about to show us a similar swiftness in butchery.

I have twenty-five Gold-beetles (*Carabus auratus*, Lin.) in a large glass vivarium. At present they are motionless, cowering under a bit of board which I gave them as a shelter. With their bellies cooled by the sand and their backs warmed by the board, which is visited by the searching rays of the sun, they slumber and digest their food. By good luck I chance upon a procession of Pine-caterpillars [1] descending from their tree in search

[1] Cf. *The Life of the Caterpillar:* chaps. i. to vi.—*Translator's Note.*

of a favourable spot for burial, the prelude to the underground cocoon. Here is an excellent herd for the slaughter-house of the Carabi.

I collect them and place them in the vivarium. The procession soon forms again; the caterpillars, about a hundred and fifty in number, move in an undulating line. They pass near the piece of board, in single file, like the Pigs at Chicago. This is the propitious moment. I let slip my wild animals, that is to say, I remove their shelter.

The sleepers forthwith awaken, scenting the rich prey defiling close at hand. One of them runs forward; three or four others follow, arousing the whole assembly; those who are buried emerge; the whole band of cut-throats falls upon the passing herd. Then comes an unforgettable sight. The mandibles get to work in all directions; the procession is attacked in the van, in the rear, in the middle; the victims are assailed in the back or the belly at random. The hairy skins are ripped open, their contents escape in a rush of entrails green with the pine-needles that constitute the food; the caterpillars writhe convulsively and lash out with their tails, suddenly coiling and uncoiling,

clinging with their feet, dribbling and biting.
Those as yet unscathed dig desperately in an
attempt to take refuge underground. Not
one succeeds. They are hardly half-way
down before the Carabus hastens up, pulls
them out and rips them open.

If the butchery were not occurring in a
dumb world, we should have all the fright-
ful hubbub of the Chicago massacres. But
it needs the ear of the imagination to hear
the shrieks and lamentations of the eviscerated. This ear I possess; and I am seized
with remorse for having provoked such sufferings.

The Beetles are now rummaging everywhere in the heap of dead and dying, each
tugging and tearing at a morsel which he
carries off to swallow privately, away from
envious eyes. After this mouthful, another
is hurriedly cut off the carcase, followed by
more still, as long as any dismembered bodies
remain. In a few minutes the procession is
reduced to a few shreds of still quivering
flesh.

There were a hundred and fifty caterpillars; the butchers are twenty-five. This
makes six victims to each Carabus. If the
insect had nothing to do but to kill indef-

initely, like the labourers in the meat-factories, and if the staff consisted of a hundred
disembowellers, a very modest figure compared with that of the ham-boners, the total
number of victims, in a ten hours' day, would
be thirty-six thousand. No Chicago can-
nery ever achieved such an output.

The speed of the assassination is even
more remarkable when we consider the difficulties of the attack. The Carabus has
nothing like the endless chain which seizes the
Pig by one leg, hoists it up and swings it
along to the butcher's knife; he has nothing
like the sliding plank which brings the Bul-
lock's forehead beneath the slaughterer's
mallet; he has to fall upon his prey, over-
power it and steer clear of its tusks and
claws. Moreover, what he disembowels he
eats on the spot. What a massacre it would
be if the insect had nothing to do but kill!

What do we learn from the Chicago
slaughter-houses and the Gold-beetle's feasting? This: the man of lofty morals is nowadays a rather rare exception. Under the
skin of the civilized being we nearly always
find the ancestor, the savage contemporary
with the Cave-bear. True humanity does
not yet exist; it is being very gradually

More Beetles

formed by the leaven of the centuries and the lessons of conscience; it is progressing towards better things with heart-breaking slowness.

It was only yesterday that slavery disappeared, the foundation of the ancient community, and that people perceived that a man, even though black, is really a man and as such deserving of consideration.

What was woman in the old days? What she still is in the East: a pretty little animal without a soul. The question was discussed at great length by the scholars. The great seventeenth-century bishop Bossuet [1] himself, looked upon woman as the diminutive of man. The proof lay in the origin of Eve: she was the superfluous bone, the thirteenth rib which Adam had in the beginning. It has at last been admitted that woman possesses a soul similar to our own and even its superior in tenderness and devotion. She has been permitted to educate herself, which she does with a zeal at least equal to that of her rival. But the law, that gloomy cavern which is still the lurking-place of so many

[1] Jacques Bénigne Bossuet, Bishop of Meaux (1627-1704),—author of many famous religious, historical and political works.—*Translator's Note.*

barbarities, continues to regard her as incompetent, as a minor.

The abolition of slavery and the education of women are two enormous strides upon the path of moral progress. Our grandchildren will go further. They will see, with a clear vision, capable of piercing every obstacle, that war is the most absurd of our eccentricities; that conquerors, fighters of battles and despoilers of nations are execrable scourges; that a hand-shake is better than a rifle-bullet; that the happiest people is not that which possesses the most artillery but that which labours in peace and produces abundantly; and that the amenities of existence do not positively clamour for frontiers, beyond which the vexatious custom-house-officer awaits us, searching our pockets and plundering our luggage.

They will see all this, our grandsons, and many other wonders which to-day rank as crazy dreams. Whither will it lead us, this ascent? Towards the blue skies of the ideal? To no very great height, I fear. We are afflicted with an indelible taint, a sort of original sin, if we may give the name of sin to a state of affairs in which our free will plays no part. We are built that way and we cannot help it. It is the taint of the belly, that inexhaustible source of brutality.

The intestine rules the world. In the midst of our gravest affairs the question of bread and butter rises imperious. So long as there are stomachs that digest—and as yet we see no possibility of dispensing with them —we must have the wherewithal to satisfy them and the strong will live by the misfortunes of the weak. Life is an abyss which only death can fill. Hence endless butcheries, on which man, Gold-beetles and others feed; hence the perpetual massacres that have made of the world a slaughter-house beside which those of Chicago hardly count.

But the feasters are legion and the victuals are not abundant in proportion. Those who have not envy those who have; the famished show their teeth to the sated. Then follows the battle for the right of possession. Man raises armies to defend his harvests, his cellars, his granaries; and this is war. Shall we ever see the end of it? Alas and seven times alas! So long as there are Wolves in the world, there must be Sheepdogs to defend the flock!

Carried away by our thoughts, we have left our Beetles far behind. Let us hurry

The Gold Beetles: Their Food

back to them. What was my reason for provoking the massacre of the Processionaries who were on the point of quietly burying themselves when I confronted them with their butchers? Was it to enjoy the spectacle of a frantic massacre? Certainly not: I have always pitied the sufferings of animals; and the life of the smallest is worthy of respect. To overcome that compassion, the demands of scientific research were needed; and these are sometimes cruel.

I had in view the habits of the Gold-beetle, the little ranger of our gardens who, for this reason, is popularly known as the Gardener. How far does he deserve to be called a helper? What does the Carabus hunt? Of what vermin does he rid our flower-beds? We have seen a promising start made with the Pine Processionary. Let us continue in the same direction.

On various occasions late in April, the enclosure provides me with processions, now longer, now shorter. I capture them and place them in the glass vivarium. No sooner is the banquet served than the feasting begins. The caterpillars are ripped open, by a single consumer or by several at one time. In less than fifteen minutes the herd is completely exterminated. Nothing remains but shapeless lumps, which are carried hither and thither to be consumed under the shelter of the board. The well-provided Beetle decamps, with his booty in his teeth, anxious to feast in peace. He is met by companions who, enticed by the morsel dangling from the fugitive's jaws, turn highwaymen. First two, then three try to rob the lawful owner. Each grabs the fragment, tugs at it, proceeds to swallow it without serious dispute. There is no actual battle, no exchange of bites as with Dogs disputing a bone. Everything is confined to attempts at theft. If the owner retains his hold, they all eat peacefully in common, mandibles touching mandibles, until the piece is torn apart and each retires with his shred.

The Pine Processionary, seasoned with that stinging poison which, during my earlier investigations, brought out such a violent rash upon my skin, must be a very pungent dish. My Carabi thoroughly enjoy it. The more processions I provide, the more they consume. The fare is highly appreciated. Nevertheless, no one, so far as I know, has ever met the Gold Beetle or her larva in the silken purses of the Bombyx.[1] I have not the slightest hope that I shall one day find them there myself. These purses are inhabited only in winter, when the Carabus, indifferent to food and overcome by torpor, lies snugly underground. But in April, when the caterpillars march in procession, seeking a good site for burial and metamorphosis, the Beetle, if he has the good luck to encounter them, must profit largely by the windfall.

The furry nature of the game does not put him off; nevertheless, the hairiest of our caterpillars, the so-called Hedgehog,[2] with its undulating mane, half-red, half-black, does seem to be too much for the glutton. For days on end it wanders about the cage in the assassins' society. The Carabi seem to ignore its presence. From time to time, one of them will stop, circumnavigate the hairy creature, examine it and try to dig into the bristling fleece. Rebuffed at once by the long, thick, hairy palisade, he retires with-

[1] The Pine Processionary is the caterpillar of the Moth known as the Pine Bombyx.—*Translator's Note.*

[2] The larva of the Tiger-moth (*Celonia caja*) Cf. *The Life of the Caterpillar:* chaps. vi. and vii.—*Translator's Note.*

out biting to the quick. Proud and unscathed, the caterpillar proceeds upon its
way with undulating back.

This cannot last. In a moment of hunger,
emboldened moreover by the co-operation of
his fellows, the poltroon decides upn a serious attack. There are four of them, very
busy around the Hedgehog, which, worried
before and behind, ends by succumbing. It
is ripped open and devoured as greedily as
any defenceless caterpillar would be.

I supply my menagerie with various caterpillars, naked or hairy, as I chance to find
them. All are accepted with the utmost
zest, on the one condition that their size is
not excessive as compared with that of the
murderer. Too small, they are despised:
the morsel would not provide an adequate
mouthful. Those of the Spurge Hawk-moth
and the Great Peacock Moth, for instance,
would suit the Carabus, were it not that, at
the first bite, the intended victim, by a twist
of its powerful rump, hurls its assailant afar.
After a few assaults, each followed by a distant tumble, the insect helplessly and regret-
fully abandons the attack. The prey is too
vigorous. I have kept the two sturdy caterpillars caged with my savage Beetles for a

fortnight; and nothing very serious has happened to them. The abrupt intervention of a suddenly lifted rump overawed the ferocious mandibles.

We will award a first good mark to the Gold Beetle, for exterminating any not too powerful caterpillar. The merit is spoilt by one flaw. The insect is not a climber: it hunts on the ground, not in the foliage overhead. I have never seen it explore the twigs of the smallest shrub. In my cages, it pays no attention to the most enticing quarry fixed to a tuft of thyme, a few inches high. This is a great pity. If the insect could only climb and undertake overhead raids, how quickly would a gang of three or four purge the cabbage of its scourge, the Pieris Caterpillar! The very best always have some defect.

The Gold Beetle must be given another good mark with reference to Slugs. He feeds on all of them, including even the biggest, the Grey Slug, flecked with dark spots. The corpulent creature is soon disposed of, when attacked by three or four knackers. They make by choice for that part of the back which is protected by an inner shell, a sort of slab of mother-of-pearl that covers the region of the heart and lung. The stony particles of which the shell is constructed abound here rather than elsewhere; and the Carabus seems to like this mineral condiment. In the same way, the favourite morsel in the Snail is the mantle, speckled with chalky dots. Easily caught and highly appreciated in flavour, the Slug, crawling at night towards the tender lettuces, must often provide the Gold Beetles with a meal. Together with the caterpillar, he appears to be the Beetle's usual fare.

We must add the Earthworm, *Lumbricus terrestris,* often found outside its burrow in rainy weather. Even the biggest do not intimidate the aggressor. I dish up an Earthworm eight inches long and as thick as my little finger. The enormous annelid is attacked as soon as seen: six Carabi come hastening up together. As its only means of defence, the victim writhes forwards and backwards, wriggling and rolling upon itself. The monstrous worm drags with it, now on top and now below, the stubborn carvers, who do not let go and work alternately in their normal position or with upturned bellies. Constantly rolling and pitching, burying itself in the sand and reappearing, it does not succeed in discouraging them. It would be difficult to find a parallel to their tenacity.

They continue to bite at the points once bitten; they hold tight and let the desperate worm flounder at will, until the tough, leathery skin ends by giving way. The contents pour forth in a blood-stained mess, into which the gluttons plunge their heads. Others hurry up to be in at the death; and soon the mighty worm is a ruin odious to look upon. I put an end to the orgy, lest the gormandizers, heavy with food, should for a long time resist the experiments which I am contemplating. Their frantic feasting tells me pretty clearly that they would finish the huge saveloy if I did not interfere.

To make amends, I throw them an Earthworm of medium size. Ripped open at different points and tugged to and fro, the worm is divided into sections which each Beetle carries off as secured and moves away to consume in seclusion. So long as the dish is not cut up, the banqueters eat peacefully among themselves, often head to head, with their mandibles fixed in the same wound; but, so soon as they feel that they have lopped off a bit that suits them, they hasten to make away with their plunder, far from any covetous envy. The bulk is general property, without strife or contest; but the particle extracted belongs to the individual and must be nimbly carried out of the reach of any thievish enterprises.

Let us vary the provisions as far as my resources will permit. Some Cetoniæ (*C. floricola*) remain in the Gold Beetles' company for a couple of weeks. They are unmolested; they are hardly vouchsafed a passing glance. Does this mean indifference to the particular game? Does it mean that the game is difficult to attack? We shall see. I remove the wings and wing-cases. The news that there are cripples about soon spreads. The Carabi hasten along and greedily root in their bellies. After a brief spell, the Cetoniæ are drained dry. The fare therefore is deemed excellent, and it was the harness of the tight wing-cases that at first intimidated the ravenous Beetles.

The result is the same with the big Black Chrysomela-beetle (*Timarcha tenebricosa*). The intact insect is disdained by the Carabus, who often encounters it in the vivarium and passes on, without trying to open the hermetically sealed meat-tin. But, if I remove the wing-cases, it is very satisfactorily devoured, notwithstanding its orange-yellow secretions.

The Gold Beetles: Their Food

Again, the same Chrysomela's fat larva, with its delicate, bare skin, makes a treat for the Carabus. Its almost metallic, bronze-black colour causes no hesitation in the hunter. As soon as seen, the tasty morsel is grabbed, ripped open and consumed. The bronze pill is regarded as a choice titbit; as many are devoured as I am able to serve.

Under the strongly-built roof of their wing-cases, the Cetonia and the Black Chrysomela are safe from the attacks of the Gold Beetle, who has not the knack of forcing open the cuirass to reach the tender abdomen. If, on the other hand, the tin is less precisely closed, the ravener finds it an easy matter to lift the defensive sheaths of his prey and attain his ends. After a few attempts, he raises the wing-cases of *Cerambyx cerdo* and of many others from behind; he opens his oyster, pushes aside the shells and lays bare the succulent dainties of the abdomen. Any Beetle is accepted, if it be possible to force open the tin.

I serve a Great Peacock, fresh from the cocoon. The Gold Beetle does not make a fierce rush for the magnificent titbit. He approaches warily at intervals, trying to nibble at the abdomen. But, at the first touch of the mandibles, the Moth grows excited, beats the ground with her wide wings and, with a sudden flap, hurls the aggressor to a distance. Attack is impossible with such game as this, for ever fluttering and giving vigorous jerks. I cut off the big Moth's wings. The assailants are soon on the spot. There are seven of them tugging and biting the cripple's belly. The down flies off in tufts, the skin breaks and the seven Beetles besetting the quarry dive into the entrails. It is like a pack of Wolves devouring a horse. In a little while the Great Peacock is eviscerated.

The Carabus has no particular liking for the Snail (*Helix aspersa*) so long as he remains intact. I place two in the midst of my Beetles, whom a couple of days' fasting has rendered more than usually enterprising. The molluscs are enscoced within their shells; and these are stuck into the sand of the cage mouth upwards. The Carabi come up and stop for a moment, in turns; they taste the slime and at once go away in disgust, without insisting further. Slightly bitten here and there, the Snail foams by driving out the small reserve of air contained in his pulmonary sac. This viscous froth constitutes his protection. The passing Beetle who takes a modest mouthful of this retires forthwith, not caring to dig any more.

The foamy covering is highly effective. I leave the two Snails all day in the presence of the famished Beetles. No disaster befalls them. Next morning I find them as fresh and fit as before. To save the Carabus from that odious froth, I lay bare the two molluscs over an expanse as wide as my thumb-nail, removing a fragment of the shell in the region of the pulmonary sac. The attack now becomes prompt and persistent.

Five or six Gold Beetles at a time take their stands around the breach that lays bare the non-slimy flesh. There would be more of them if there were room for a greater number, for some eager Carabi arrive who try to slip in between the occupants. Above the breach a sort of scrimmage forms, in which those nearest the victim dig and uproot its flesh, while the others look on or steal a bit from their neighbour's lips. In one afternoon, the Snail is emptied almost to the bottom of his spiral.

Next day, when the carnage is at its height, I remove the prey and replace it by an untouched Snail, fixed in the sand with

the opening at the top. Aroused by a bath
of water, the animal comes out of its shell,
protruding its swan-like neck and extending
to their full length its telescopic eye-stalks,
which seem quite placidly to contemplate
the frantic saraband of the ravenous Beetles.
The imminent danger of evisceration does
not prevent it from fully displaying its tender flesh, an easy prey on which, one would
think, the gluttons, deprived of their meat,
will fling themselves to continue the interrupted feast.

But what is this? None of the Gold
Beetles pays any attention to the magnificent
quarry, which, swaying with a wave-like motion, is largely uncovered by its fortress. If
one of the starvelings, more greatly daring
than the others, ventures to dig a tooth into
the mollusc, the Snail contracts, goes indoors
and begins to foam. This is enough to re-
pel the assailant. All the afternoon and all
night, the victim remains thus in the presence
of five-and-twenty disembowellers; and nothing serious happens.

This same experiment, repeated on sundry
occasions, proves that the Gold Beetle does
not attack the unwounded Snail, even when
the latter, after a shower of rain, is crawling

The Gold Beetles: Their Food

over the wet grass, protruding all the fore-part of his body from the shell. The Cara-bus wants cripples, helpless inmates of bro-ken shells; he wants a breach which enables him to bite at a point not liable to slaver. In these circumstances, the "Gardener" can do little to restrain the Snail's misdeeds. When injured by accident, more or less badly crushed, the ravager of our garden stuff would soon die without the Gold Beetle's intervention.

From time to time, to vary the diet, I feed a piece of butcher's meat to my charges. The Carabi eagerly flock around it, diligently taking up their stand, mincing it into tiny morsels and devouring it. This food, un-known to their race save perhaps in the form of a Mole disembowelled by the peasant's spade, suits them as well as does the cater-pillar. They like any sort of meat, except-ing fish-meat. One day the bill of fare con-sisted of a Sardine. The guzzlers came trotting up, took a few mouthfuls and then withdrew without touching it again. It was too much of a novelty for them.

I must not forget to mention that the cage is provided with a drinking-trough, that is to say, a saucer full of water. The Gold

More Beetles

Beetles often come and drink at it after their meals. Parched after their heating diet and, moreover, daubed all over with slime after cutting up a Snail, they quench their thirst at the saucer, rinse their mouths and bathe their tarsi, which are shod in sticky boots heavy with sand. After this ablution, they make for their shelter under the bit of board and quietly enjoy a long siesta.

CHAPTER XIV

THE GOLD BEETLES : THEIR NUPTIAL HABITS

IT is admitted that, as an ardent destroyer of caterpillars and Slugs, the Gold Beetle has pre-eminently earned his title of "Gardener": he is the watchful keeper of our kitchen-gardens and our flower-borders. If my enquiries add nothing to his established reputation in this respect, they will at least, in what follows, display the insect in an as yet unsuspected light. The ferocious eater, the ogre devouring any prey not beyond his powers, is eaten in his turn. And by whom? By his own kin and many others.

We will begin by naming two of his enemies, the Fox and the Toad, who, in hard times, for lack of anything better, do not disdain such lean and caustic mouthfuls. When telling the story of the Trox, I described how the excreta of the Fox, which are easily recognized by the Rabbit's-fur whereof they largely consist, are sometimes encrusted with Gold Beetles' wing-cases: the ordure is adorned with sheets of gold. This testifies to the bill of fare. It is not highly nourishing nor particularly plentiful and it tastes bitter; but, after all, a few Carabi help to stay the appetite a little.

As regards the Toad, I have similar evidence. In summer, in the garden-paths, from time to time I happen on some curious objects whose origin at first leaves me quite undecided. They are small black sausages, the thickness of my little finger, which crumble very easily after drying in the sun. We recognize a conglomeration of Ants' heads and nothing besides, unless it be some remnants of slender leg. What can this singular product be, this granular amalgam consisting of hundreds and hundreds of heads packed close together?

One's mind turns to a ball disgorged by the Owl after the nourishing part has been sorted by the stomach. Further reflection discards the idea: a nocturnal bird of prey, though fond of insects, does not feed on such tiny game as this. To catch on the sticky tip of the tongue such very small fry and to collect them one by one calls for a consumer endowed with plenty of time and patience. Who is it? Could it be the

Toad? I see no other in the enclosure to whom I can attribute a salmagundy of Ants. Experiment will solve the riddle for us.

I have an old acquaintance in the garden and I know where he lives. We often meet at the hour of my evening rounds. He looks at me with his gold-yellow eyes and gravely passes on to attend to his business. He is a Toad big enough to fill a saucer, a veteran respected by the whole household. We call him the Philosopher. I apply to him to elucidate the question of the conglomerations of Ants' heads.

I imprison him in a cage, without any food, and wait until the contents of his sated paunch undergo the labours of digestion. Things do not take very long. After a few days' time, the prisoner presents me with a specimen of black ordure, moulded into a cylinder, exactly resembling those which I observe on the paths of the enclosure. It is, like the others, an amalgam of Ants' heads. I restore the Philosopher to liberty. Thanks to him, the problem which puzzled me so greatly is solved: I know for certain that the Toad is a great eater of Ants, a very small quarry, it is true, but easy to collect and inexhaustible.

More Beetles

It is not always a free choice on his part. He prefers larger mouthfuls when available. He lives mainly on Ants because they abound in the enclosure, whereas the other insects running on the surface of the ground are comparatively scarce. If occasionally the glutton finds more sumptuous fare, he appreciates the feast all the more highly.

In evidence of these unusual banquets, I will mention certain dejecta found in the enclosure and composed almost entirely of Gold Beetles' wing-cases. The remainder of the product, the paste joining the golden scales together, consisted of Ants' heads, the authentic work of the consumer. So the Toad feeds on Carabi when he has the opportunity. He, our garden helper, robs us of another helper no less valuable. The useful, from our point of view, destroys the useful: a little lesson which should modify our ingenuous belief that all things are created for our service.

There is worse to come. The Gold Beetle, the policeman who, in our gardens, keeps an eye on the misdeeds of the caterpillar and the Slug, is guilty of the vice of cannibalism. One day, in the shadow of the plane-trees outside my door, I see one passing very busily. The pilgrim is welcome: he will increase by one the colony in my vivarium. As I capture him, I perceive that the tips of his wing-cases are slightly damaged. Is this the result of a fight between rivals? There is nothing to tell me. The great thing is that the Beetle should not be handicapped by a serious injury. I examine him, find that he is unwounded and fit for service and put him among the twenty-five occupants of the glass cage.

Next day, I look for the new inmate. He is dead. His comrades have attacked him during the night and cleaned out his abdomen, which was inadequately protected by the injured wing-cases. The operation was very neatly done, without any mutilation. Legs, head, corselet are all in their right places; only the abdomen has a wide opening through which its contents have been removed. What we see is a sort of golden shell formed of two connected wing-cases. An Oyster-shell emptied of its mollusc looks no cleaner.

This result astonishes me, for I take very good care that the cage is never without provisions. The Snail, the Cockchafer, the Praying Mantis, the Earthworm, the caterpillar and other favourite dishes alternate in my refectory in more than sufficient quantities. My Gold Beetles therefore had not the excuse of hunger in devouring a brother whose damaged armour lent itself to easy attack.

Can it be their custom to finish off the wounded and to ransack the stomach of an injured kinsman? Pity is unknown among the insects. At the sight of the desperate struggles of a crippled relation, not one of the same race will stop, not one will try to help him. With carnivorous insects, matters may take an even more tragic turn. Sometimes the passers-by will run up to the invalid. Do they do so in order to assist him? Not at all: they do it to see what he tastes like and, if they find him good, to cure his ills thoroughly by devouring him.

It is therefore possible that the Carabus with the damaged wing-cases tempted his comrades by the sight of his partly denuded body. They saw in their helpless brother a prey which it was lawful to dissect. But do they respect one another when there is no previous injury? At first sight, everything would seem to show that their relations are very peaceful. There is never any scuffling between the feasters at their meals, nothing but mouth-to-mouth robberies. Nor are there any quarrels during the long siestas under the cover of the board. Half-buried in the cool earth, my five-and-twenty specimens quietly slumber and digest their food, at no great distance one from the other, each in his little trench. If I take away the shelter, they awake, make off, run hither and thither, constantly meeting without molesting one another.

Profound peace therefore prevails and seems likely to last for ever when, on inspecting the cage during the first heats of June, I find a dead Carabus. His limbs are intact; he is very neatly reduced to a mere golden husk; he shows us once more what we saw in the helpless Beetle who was lately devoured; he reminds us of the shell of the eaten Oyster. I examine the remains. But for the huge breach in the abdomen, all is as it should be. So the insect was in good health when the others gutted it.

A few days later, yet another Carabus is slain and treated like the others, with all the various pieces of the armour undisturbed. If we lay him on his belly, he seems as though intact; if we lay him on his back, he is hollow, without a scrap of flesh left inside his carapace. A little later I find another empty relic, then another, and yet another, until my menagerie is rapidly diminishing. If this frenzied slaughter continues, I shall soon have nothing left in the vivarium.

Can it be that my Gold Beetles, worn out by age, die a natural death or that the females batten on the corpses, or is the population being reduced at the expense of hale and hearty subjects? It is not easy to elucidate the matter, for the disembowelling usually takes place at night. Nevertheless, by exerting vigilance, I twice succeed in observing the autopsy by daylight.

In the middle of June, before my eyes a female sets to work upon a male, whom I recognize as such by his rather smaller size. The operation begins. Lifting the ends of the wing-cases, the assailant seizes her victim by the tip of the abdomen, on the dorsal surface. Eagerly she tugs and munches. The captive, though in the pink of condition, does not defend himself, does not turn round. He pulls his hardest in the opposite direction, to release himself from the terrible mandibles; he moves this way or that, according as he is dragging his aggressor or being dragged by her; and here his resistance ends. The combat lasts a quarter of an hour. Other Beetles passing by, stop, as though to say:

"My turn next."

At last, redoubling his efforts, the male frees himself and escapes. No doubt, if he had not succeeded in getting away, he would have had his belly gutted by the fearsome dame.

A few days later I witness a similar scene, but this time the tragedy is completed. Once more it is a female who seizes a male from behind. The bitten one submits with no more protest than his vain efforts to release himself. The skin at last gives way, the wound widens, the viscera are rooted out and swallowed by the matron, who empties the carapace with her head buried in her compeer's belly. The tremors of the poor wretch's legs announce his approaching end. The murderess takes no notice and continues to rummage as far up as the narrow entrance to the thorax allows her to go. Nothing is left of the deceased but the wing-cases, packed boat-wise, and the fore-part of the body, which is not disjointed. The empty remains are abandoned where they lie.

More Beetles

So must have perished the Gold Beetles, always males, whose relics I find from time to time in the cage; thus the survivors too must perish. Between the middle of June and the first of August, the inmates, numbering twenty-five at the outset, are reduced to five females. All the twenty males have disappeared, ripped open and drained dry. And by whom? Apparently by the females.

This is borne out by the two assaults which chance permitted me to witness; twice, in broad daylight, I saw the female devour the male after opening his belly under the wing-cases, or at least trying to do so. As for the rest of the murders, though direct observation be lacking, I have one very valuable piece of evidence. As we have seen, the captive does not retaliate, does not defend himself; he merely strives to escape by pulling as hard as he can.

If it were a simple fight, an ordinary scuffle such as life's rivalries may lead to, the Beetle attacked would obviously turn round, since he is in a position to do so; in a close tussle, he would retort on the aggressor and give bite for bite. His strength enables him to wage a battle which might turn to his advantage; and the fool allows his rump to be gnawed with impunity. It looks as though an invincible repugnance prevents him from retaliating by eating a bit of her who is eating him.

This tolerance reminds me of the Languedocian Scorpion,[1] who, after his wedding, allows himself to be devoured by his mate without using his weapon, the poisoned sting which is quite capable of killing the virago; it reminds me of the Praying Mantis' swain, who is sometimes reduced to a mere stump and, in spite of all, continues his unfinished work while he is being chewed in little mouthfuls, without the least expression of revolt.[2] These are nuptial rites against which the male is not entitled to protest.

The males in my collection of Gold Beetles, from the first to the last eviscerated, tell us of similar habits. They are the victims of their mates when these have had their fill of matrimony. During four months, from April to July, couples form daily, sometimes only tentatively, sometimes and more often concluding in effective pairing. There

[1] The seven essays on the Languedocian Scorpion will appear in the final volume of the series, entitled *The Life of the Scorpion.—Translator's Note.*

[2] Cf. *The Life of the Grasshopper:* chaps. vi. to ix. and, in particular, chap. vii.—*Translator's Note.*

is no end to it with these fiery temperaments.

The Carabus is expeditious in his love-affairs. A male passing in the crowd flings himself upon a female, the first that comes, without any previous flirting. The she thus bestridden lifts her head a little as a sign of acquiesence, while her rider whips her neck with the tips of his antennæ. When the coupling is finished—and it does not take long—the two separate abruptly, recuperate their strength by a mouthful of the Snail served up for their food, after which they both get married again, the wedding being repeated so long as males remain available. After feasting, a brutal wooing; after the wooing, more feasting: this sums up the Gold Beetle's life.

The ladies in my menagerie were not in proportion to the number of suitors: there were five females to twenty males. No matter: there was no rivalry, no exchange of blows; a most peaceful use and abuse was made of the passing fair. With this mutual tolerance, sooner or later, many times over and according to the chance of the encounters, each one finds the wherewithal to satisfy his ardour.

I should have preferred a more evenly

divided assembly. Luck, not choice, gave me that which I had at my disposal. I collected in early spring all the Gold Beetles that I could find under the stones around, without distinction of sex, which is not easy to recognize merely by external characteristics. Afterwards, as I reared them in my cages, I learnt that a slight excess in size was the distinctive sign of the females. My menagerie, so unequal in the numerical relation of the sexes, was therefore a fortuitous result. It seems likely that this proportion of males does not exist under natural conditions.

On the other hand, such numerous groups are never seen at liberty, sheltered under the same stone. The Gold Beetle leads an almost solitary life; it is rare to find two or three gathered at one spot. The assembly in my menagerie is therefore exceptional, although it does not lead to disorder. There is plenty of room in the glass cage for distant rambles and for all the usual diversions. He who wants to be alone remains alone; he who wants company soon finds it.

For that matter, captivity does not seem to trouble them unduly, as is shown by the frequent feasting and their daily repeated mating. They could thrive no better if at liberty in the fields: perhaps they would not thrive so well, for food is not so abundant there as in the cage. As regards comfort, therefore, the prisoners are in a normal condition favouring the preservation of their usual habits.

Only, meetings of kinsfolk occur more often here than in the open. This, no doubt, affords the females better opportunities to persecute the males for whom they have no further use, to grab them by the rump and disembowel them. This hunting of the bygone lovers is aggravated but certainly not innovated by the too close vicinity: such customs are never improvised.

When the mating is over, a female meeting a male in the open must then treat him as fair game and munch him up in order to close the matrimonial rites. I have turned over many stones but have never chanced upon this spectacle; no matter: what I saw in the cage is enough to convince me. What a world the Gold Beetle lives in, where the matron devours her partner when she no longer needs him to fertilize her ovaries! And how lightly do the laws of creation hold the males, to allow them to be butchered in this way!

Gold Beetles: Their Nuptial Habits

Are these fits of cannibalism following upon love widely distributed? For the moment I know only three really characteristic examples: those of the Praying Mantis, the Languedocian Scorpion and the Golden Carabus. The horror of the lover converted into prey is also found in the Locustian tribe, though accompanied by less brutality, for the victim devoured is now a dead and not a living insect. The female of the White-faced Decticus [1] is quite willing to nibble a leg of the defunct male. The Green Grasshopper [2] behaves likewise.

To a certain degree the nature of the diet acts as an excuse: Dectici and Grasshoppers are first and foremost carnivores. Coming upon a corpse of their own species, the matrons consume it more or less thoroughly, even if it be that of last night's lover. Considered as game, one is as good as another.

But what shall we say of the vegetarians? As the laying-season approaches, the Ephippiger turns upon her companion, still full of life, and bites him, makes a hole in his belly and eats as much of him as her appetite al-

[1] Cf. *The Life of the Grasshopper:* chaps. xi. to xiii. and, in particular, chap. xi.—*Translator's Note.*
[2] Cf. *idem:* chap. xiv.—*Translator's Note.*

lows. The easy-going Cricket suddenly develops a shrewish character: she beats the mate who lately wooed her in such impassioned serenades; she rends his wings, breaks his fiddle and even goes so far as to tear a few mouthfuls from the musician.[1] So it seems probable that this mortal aversion of the female for the male after the pairing is fairly common, especially among the carnivorous insects. What is the reason of these atrocious habits? If circumstances favour me, I shall not fail to investigate it.

Of the whole colony in the cage I have five females left at the beginning of August. Their conduct has changed greatly since the eating of the males. Food has become indifferent to them. They no longer run up to the Snail, whom I serve half-stripped of his shell; they scorn the plump Mantis and the Caterpillar, their erstwhile delights; they doze under the shelter of the board and rarely show themselves. Can this mean preparation for the laying? I enquire into this day by day, being most anxious to see the first appearance of the little larvæ, an artless first appearance, deprived of all so-

[1] Cf. *The Life of the Grasshopper:* chap. xvi.—*Translator's Note.*

licitude, as I foresee from the lack of industry in the mother.

I wait in vain: there is no laying. Meanwhile the cool nights of October arrive. Four females perish, this time by a natural death.

The survivor takes no notice of them. She refuses them burial in her stomach, a burial at one time accorded to the males, dissected alive. She cowers as deep down in the ground as the scanty earth of the cage permits. In November, when Mont Ventoux is white with the first snows, she grows torpid in her hiding-place. Let us henceforth leave her in peace. She will live through the winter, everything seems to tell us, and produce her eggs next spring.

Index

A

Acherontia atropos, (*see*
 Death's Hawk-Moth)
Adder, 35, 39
Ægosonia, (*see Ae scrab-
 ricorne*), 191, 204, 228
Aleochra fuscipes, 49
African Leguminosa, (*see*
 Archis)
African Scarabus, 247
Ajaccio, 247
Algeria, 247
Alstræmeria pelegrina, (*see*
 Inca Lily)
A. moschata, (*see* Rose-
 scented Aromia)
Anoxia, 24, 53, 213
Anthophoræ, 2, 86
Ants, 300, 301
Apicus, Marcus Gabius,
 178
Arachis, 210
Ariadne, 72
Atenchus, 259
Attelabus Beetle, 223

B

Baucis, 98
Beaded Trox, 55-71
Bees, 2, 3, 86, 242, 243, 265,
 273
Bison Ortis, 126

Big-Jawed Staphlinus, 49,
 54
Bitter Sweet, 225
Black-berried Nightshade,
 225
Black Chrysomela, 293
Bolboceras, 203, 205
Bossuet, Jacques B., 282
Brachycerus algirus, 226
Brillat-Savarin, Anthelme,
 183
Broad-necked Scarab, 258
Bruchus, 216
Buprestes, 198, 216
Burrow, The, (*see Mino-
 taurus Typhœus*)
Burying Beetle, 42, 47
Butterfly, 3, 4, 264

C

Cabbage Butterfly, 3, 4
Candide, 167
Capricorn, 175, 176, 178,
 187, 188, 189, 191, 199,
 203, 204, 205, 207, 208,
 209, 228, 234, 235, 264,
 293
Carabus, 63, 198, 216
Carabus auratus, (*see* Gold
 Beetle)
Caterpillar, 216, 278, 289,
 299, 314

317

Index

Index

319

Index

Index

Index